THE
NOSTALGIA QUIZ
BOOK #2

the nostalgia Quiz book

#2

Martin A. Gross

ARLINGTON HOUSE·PUBLISHERS
NEW ROCHELLE, N. Y.

Library of Congress Catalog Card Number 74–1425

Manufactured in the United States of America

Library of Congress Cataloging in Publication Data

Gross, Martin Arnold, 1934–
    The nostalgia quiz book #2

    1. Questions and answers. I. Title.
[AG195.G682]   031'.02   74-1425
ISBN 0-87000-259-7

TO MY BROTHER RICHARD,
WHOSE COMIC-BOOK COLLECTION
WAS LARGER THAN MINE

INTRODUCTION

With over 75,000 hard-cover and paperback copies in print of the premier book in this series—*The Nostalgia Quiz Book*—the evidence points to a burgeoning interest in our immediate past.

There are many reasons for this nostalgia boom—a new appreciation of yesterday's popular culture . . . a turning away from the myriad problems of today . . . a richer awareness of our history and heritage—but the answer is far simpler than that. It's just a lot of fun to sit back and try to recall the stars of the movies you saw on Saturday afternoon . . . the TV programs that once flickered through the ether (remember when Tuesday night was Berle night?) . . . the radio programs that drew you into the action by requiring you to visualize the scene . . . the comic strips and comic books peopled by strange, fantastic characters who didn't go to school, didn't have to practice the piano or cross at the corner . . . the sports figures who were Olympian in their grandeur . . . and swing bands that made music that echoes down the caverns of the years.

In *The Nostalgia Quiz Book #2* you'll find all these memories categorized—sometimes neatly, sometimes arbitrarily—and turned into quizzes. It's a giant history test that you can grade yourself and that nobody can really flunk. The answers are in the back of the book, and if the questions evoke a host of memories, the answers will spark still another exercise in Total Recall.

Whether you use the book to test your own nostalgia knowhow, or try to stump your friends—you'll earn a dividend far and beyond that of just knowing the answers . . . you'll be able to take a trip into the past, your past. As Alexander Smith, a writer remembered today, if at all, mainly for his plaintive plea, "To be occasionally quoted is the only fame I care for," once observed: "A man's real possession is his memory. In nothing else is he rich."

1.   MATINEE IDYLLS

1. Name three Abbott and Costello "military" movies.

*   *   *

2. Warner Baxter won a Best Actor Oscar for *In Old Arizona.* For what movie did Alice Brady win her Best Supporting Actress Oscar?

*   *   *

3. What actress was featured in all four of these "love" movies: *Three Cheers for Love, It's Love I'm After, She Loved a Fireman,* and *Love, Honor and Goodbye?*

*   *   *

4. What actor was featured in all five of these "lively" movies: *The Man Who Lived Twice, You Only Live Once, Hitler—Dead or Alive, It's a Wonderful Life,* and *The Time of Your Life?*

*   *   *

5. What actor was featured in all four of these "musical" films: *The Desert Song, Song of the West, King of Jazz,* and *Music in the Air?*

*   *   *

6. What actor was featured in all three of these "Far Easterns": *South Sea Rose, East of Borneo,* and *Burma Convoy?*

*   *   *

7. What were the two roles played by Leon Errol in *The Mexican Spitfire* series?

*   *   *

8. Who played Edgar Kennedy's screen wife?

*   *   *

9. Ed "Pop" Martin was played by a) Harry Langdon; b) Andy Clyde; c) W. C. Fields; or d) Robert Benchley?

*   *   *

10. Name the two great comediennes who appeared in the Thelma Todd comedy shorts.

†   †   †

2. DIAL TONES

† † † † †

Match the creator and the radio show:

1. Christopher Morley   a) "Major Hoople"
2. Gene Ahern   b) "Tillie the Toiler"
3. Brett Halliday   c) "Michael Shayne, Private Detective"
4. Frances and Richard   d) "Of Human Bondage" Lockridge
5. Isabel Scott Rorick   e) "Kitty Foyle"
6. Somerset Maugham   f) "Mr. and Mrs. North"
7. Erle Stanley Gardner   g) "Perry Mason"
8. Olive Higgins Prouty   h) "My Favorite Husband"
9. Russ Westover   i) "Stella Dallas"

† † †

3. REEL QUESTIONS

1. Lyle Talbot starred in *Red Hot Tires.* What was James Cagney's racing movie?

* * *

2. Name two movies about Mexico starring Paul Muni.

* * *

3. Brenda Marshall starred in *Singapore Woman.* What was William Powell's "Singapore" movie?

* * *

4. Kenny Baker was in *Mr. Dodd Takes the Air.* What was Ronald Reagan's "radio" movie?

* * *

5. Barry Fitzgerald was in *The Story of Seabiscuit.* What was Sam Levene's "racing" movie?

* * *

6. Whose band was featured in *Thank Your Lucky Stars, Bring on the Girls, Variety Girl,* and *Fireman Save My Child?*

* * *

7. Where did *Journey into Fear* take place?

*   *   *

8. Who wrote the novels inspiring these movies: *Jamaica Inn, Frenchman's Creek, Rebecca, My Cousin Rachel,* and *The Birds?*

*   *   *

9. Who was the Spanish artist who played an important part in the making of *An Andalusian Dog* and *L'Age d'Or?*

*   *   *

10. Who shot Jennifer Jones to death in *Duel in the Sun?*

†   †   †

13

4. STAR BOOKING

† † † † †

Match the autobiography with its author:

1. *My Wicked, Wicked Ways*   a) Frank Capra
2. *Wings on My Feet*   b) William S. Hart
3. *Have Tux, Will Travel*   c) Helen Traubel
4. *It Took Nine Tailors*   d) William Gargan
5. *St. Louis Woman*   e) Sophie Tucker
6. *Some of These Days*   f) Adolph Menjou
7. *My Time Is Your Time*   g) Sonja Henie
8. *Why Me?*   h) Bob Hope
9. *The Name Above the Title*   i) Errol Flynn
10. *My Life East and West*   j) Rudy Vallee

† † †

5.   HOLLYWOOD BASEBALL

† † † † †

Match the baseball movie with the star:

1. *Elmer the Great*   a) Gene Kelly
2. *Warming Up*   b) James Stewart
3. *Hot Curves*   c) William Bendix
4. *It Happened in Flatbush*   d) Jack Oakie
5. *The Babe Ruth Story*   e) Joe E. Brown
6. *The Stratton Story*   f) Lloyd Nolan
7. *Speedy*   g) Ray Milland
8. *Take Me Out*   h) Paul Douglas
   to the Ball Game
9. *The Kid from Left Field*   i) George Brent
10. *Rhubarb*   j) Dan Dailey
11. *Angels in the Outfield*   k) Tom Ewell
12. *The Kid from Cleveland*   l) Harold Lloyd
13. *Fast Company*   m) Richard Dix
14. *The Great American*   n) Bennie Rubin
    Pastime

† † †

6. LOOKING FOR YESTERDAY

1. Who was Jafsie Condon?

* * *

2. Who was Manuel Quezon?

* * *

3. Lincoln Ellsworth explored what region by plane?

* * *

4. The Society of Friends and Enemies of Modern Music presented what new opera in 1934?

* * *

5. Stout Airlines—the first airline to carry mail—was owned by a man who refused to open his Detroit airport on Sunday. Who was he?

* * *

6. "Ol' Man River" in *Till the Clouds Roll By* was sung by a) Tony Martin; b) Johnny Johnston; or c) Frank Sinatra?

* * *

7. "They're Either Too Young or Too Old" in *Thank Your Lucky Stars* was sung by a) Alexis Smith; b) Olivia De Havilland; c) Bette Davis; d) Joan Leslie; or e) Ann Sheridan?

* * *

8. Special delivery in 1928 cost a) 50¢; b) $1.00;
c) 25¢; or d) 10¢?

* * *

9. Who was the heavyweight boxing champion who
lectured on Shakespeare at Yale University?

* * *

10. The British pound sterling was valued in 1928 at
a) $10.00; b) $7.75; c) $4.86; or d) $2.50?

† † †

7. MOVIE MEDICS

† † † † †

Match the medical movie with the star:

1. *Doctor Bull*	a) Robert Taylor
2. *Welcome Stranger*	b) Robert Donat
3. *A Man to Remember*	c) Rock Hudson
4. *Wife, Doctor and Nurse*	d) Bing Crosby
5. *Society Doctor*	e) Macdonald Carey
6. *Magnificent Obsession*	f) June Allyson
7. *Dr. X*	g) Will Rogers
8. *Dr. Broadway*	h) Sidney Blackmer
9. *Patient in Room 18*	i) Aline MacMahon
10. *Vigil in the Night*	j) Warner Baxter
11. *Girl in White*	k) Carole Lombard
12. *A Doctor's Diary*	l) Lionel Atwill
13. *The Citadel*	m) Edward Ellis

† † †

8. CHANNEL CHALLENGES

1. Ken Lynch's face was never seen, although he was the star of what show?

* * *

2. Stacy Harris "investigated crucial social and political situations" on what show?

* * *

3. Craig Stevens played Peter Gunn. Who played his girl friend?

* * *

4. Name the stars of a) "87th Precinct"; b) "Johnny Staccato"; c) "Coronado 9"; and d) "Boston Blackie."

* * *

5. Who was TV's Charlie Chan?

* * *

6. Who played a) Mike Hammer; b) Markham; c) Sherlock Holmes; d) Richard Diamond?

* * *

7. Who covered Times Square as columnist Johnny Warren?

* * *

8. Before "I Spy" there was "I Spy." Name the star of the original show.

*   *   *

9. Who were the Four Just Men?

*   *   *

10. Identify a) "The Man Called X"; b) "The Hunter"; c) "The Lone Wolf."

†   †   †

20

9.   POPCORN QUERIES

1. *Seventh Heaven* was directed by a) Howard Hawks; b) Frank Borzage; c) Robert Siodmak; or d) Mervyn LeRoy?

* * *

2. *You Can't Take It with You* was directed by a) Leo McCarey; b) Henry Hathaway; c) Tay Garnett; or d) Frank Capra?

* * *

3. *Camille* was directed by a) George Cukor; Raoul Walsh; c) Victor Fleming; or d) Alfred Hitchcock?

* * *

4. *Grand Hotel* was directed by a) Henry Hathaway; b) Michael Curtiz; c) Edmund Goulding; or d) Ernst Lubitsch?

* * *

5. *Casablanca* was directed by a) Nicholas Ray; b) Billy Wilder; c) Michael Curtiz; or d) George Cukor?

* * *

6. *The Wizard of Oz* was directed by a) Walt Disney; b) Victor Fleming; c) Leo McCarey; or d) Robert Siodmak?

* * *

7. *The Postman Always Rings Twice* was directed by

21

a) Alfred Hitchcock; b) Raoul Walsh; c) Robert Siodmak; or d) Tay Garnett?

* * *

8. *The Lives of a Bengal Lancer* was directed by a) Zoltan Korda; b) Henry Hathaway; c) Howard Hawks; or d) Victor Fleming?

* * *

9. *Scarface* was directed by a) Robert Siodmak; b) Frank Borzage; c) Howard Hawks; or d) Nicholas Ray?

* * *

10. *I Am a Fugitive from a Chain Gang* was directed by a) Mervyn LeRoy; b) Edmund Goulding; c) Michael Curtiz; or d) Victor Fleming?

10. TOUCHDOWN MATTERS

† † † † †

Match the position and at least one team with the Professional Football Hall of Famer:

1. Cliff Battles	a) end	I. Chicago Bears
2. Sammy Baugh	b) center	II. Chicago Cardinals
3. Dutch Clark	c) halfback	III. Boston Braves
4. John Driscoll	d) fullback	IV. Washington Redskins
5. Turk Edwards	e) quarterback	V. Cleveland Rams
6. Otto Graham	f) tackle	VI. Cleveland Browns
7. Mel Hein	g) guard	VII. New York Giants
8. Clarke Hinkle		VIII. Philadelphia Eagles
9. Don Hutson		IX. Portsmouth Spartans
10. George McAfee		X. Detroit Lions
11. Bulldog Turner		XI. Green Bay Packers
12. George Trafton		
13. Pete Pihos		
14. Dan Fortmann		

† † †

11. HOLLYWOOD HELL

Match the clue with the Satanic Movie:

1. Jean Arthur starred in this department-store story, where magnate Charles Coburn takes a job in his own emporium.
2. Gary Cooper and Cary Grant were after Tallulah's hand in this submarine saga.
3. Father Spencer Tracy tried to evacuate a hospital one step ahead of the lava.
4. Bela, Bela raised a pet.
5. Boris tries to talk to his dead wife.
6. Lionel Barrymore shrinks bodies for fun and revenge.
7. Freddie Bartholomew, Mickey Rooney, and Jackie Cooper in a two-hankie mellerdrama.
8. Marlene Dietrich makes trouble for Spanish revolutionaries.
9. Some more tea; some more talk; some more Colman, Young, and Loy, m'dear?
10. Ollie and Stan in a remake of an operetta.

   a) *The Devil Is a Sissy*
   b) *The Devil to Pay*
   c) *The Devil and Miss Jones*
   d) *The Devil's Brother*
   e) *The Devil Bat*
   f) *The Devil Is a Woman*
   g) *Devil and the Deep*
   h) *The Devil Commands*
   i) *The Devil at 4 O'Clock*
   j) *The Devil Doll*

12. MUSIC-MAKERS

† † † † †

Match the 1938 bands and vocalists:

1. Count Basie
2. Bunny Berigan
3. Larry Clinton
4. Bob Crosby

5. Jimmy Dorsey
6. Paul Whiteman
7. Chick Webb
8. Artie Shaw

9. Horace Heidt
10. Duke Ellington

a) Billie Holiday
b) Lysbeth Hughes, Larry Cotton
c) Helen Humes, James Rushing
d) Marion Mann, Nappy Lamare, Eddie Miller
e) Ivy Anderson
f) Bob Eberly, Don Mattison
g) Ella Fitzgerald
h) Joan Edwards, Jack Teagarden
i) Bea Wain, Jack Chesleigh
j) Jayne Dover, Dick Morgan

† † †

25

13. HALLOWEEN MATINEE

✝ ✝ ✝ ✝ ✝

Match the monster with the actor:
The Frankenstein monster in:
1. *Ghost of Frankenstein*
2. *Frankenstein Meets the Wolf Man*
3. *House of Frankenstein*
4. *The Curse of Frankenstein*
5. *I Was a Teenage Frankenstein*
6. *The Revenge of Frankenstein*

The Mummy in:
7. *The Mummy's Hand*
8. *The Mummy's Tomb*

The Wolf Man in:
9. *Frankenstein Meets the Wolf Man*
10. *I Was a Teenage Werewolf*
11. *Curse of the Werewolf*

The Were-Cat in:
12. *Catman of Paris*
13. *Cat People*
14. *Cat Girl*
15. *The Creeper*

a) Tom Tyler
b) Michael Landon
c) Onslow Stevens
d) Simone Simon
e) Barbara Shelley
f) Glenn Strange
g) Oliver Reed
h) Michael Gwynn
i) Christopher lee
j) Whitt Bissell
k) Lon Chaney, Jr.
l) Bela Lugosi
m) Robert Wolke

✝ ✝ ✝

14.   BIG DIAL

† † † † †

Match the star and his radio show:

1. Brian Donlevy   a) "Box 13"
2. Lionel Barrymore   b) "His Honor, the Barber"
3. Wendell Corey   c) "Mayor of the Town"
4. Herbert Marshall   d) "Front Page Farrell"
5. Ralph Bellamy   e) "Dangerous Assignment"
6. Alan Ladd   f) "Man against Crime"
7. Dick Powell   g) "McGarry and His
                            Mouse"
8. Richard Widmark   h) "A Man Called X"
9. Ronald Colman   i) "Final Edition"
10. Barry Fitzgerald   j) "The Halls of Ivy"

† † †

15. DO IT AGAIN

† † † † †

Match the original with its remake:

1. *Mad About Music*
2. *Svengali*

3. *The Male Animal*
4. *The Man Who Played God*

5. *London after Midnight*
6. *Midnight*
7. *Ballerina*

8. *Rain*

9. *3 Blind Mice*

10. *Moon Over Miami*

11. *Morning Glory*
12. *My Favorite Wife*

13. *The Narrow Corner*

14. *Folies Bergere*

15. *Marriage Circle*
16. *Strawberry Blonde*

a) *Isle of Fury*
b) *One Saturday Afternoon*
c) *Toy Tiger*
d) *One Hour with You*
e) *The Mad Genius*
f) *Stagestruck*
g) *She's Working Her Way through College*
h) *Move over, Darling*
i) *Moon over Miami*
j) *Mark of the Vampire*
k) *Sincerely Yours*
l) *Three Little Girls in Blue*
m) *Masquerade in Mexico*
n) *Miss Sadie Thompson*
o) *On the Riviera*
p) *The Man in Her Life.*

† † †

16. THEIR BIGGEST FANS

Match the autobiography with its author:

1. *Treadmill to Oblivion*   a) Pat O'Brien
2. *Up the Years from*   b) Bette Davis
   Bloomsbury
3. *I Wanted to Be an Actress* c) Gertrude Lawrence
4. *The Lonely Life*   d) Basil Rathbone
5. *The Wind at My Back*   e) Fred Allen
6. *In and Out of Character* f) Mae West
7. *A Star Danced*   g) Mickey Rooney
8. *Goodness Had Nothing*   h) George Arliss
   to Do with It
9. *My Young Life*   i) Katharine Cornell
10. *I.E.*   j) Shirley Temple

17. BAD GUYS AND GALS

† † † † †

1. Charlie in *Shadow of a Doubt* was played by
_____.

* * *

2. Maddelina in *The Paradine Case* was played by
_____.

* * *

3. Robert in *Christmas Holiday* was played by _____.

* * *

4. Elsa in *The Lady from Shanghai* was played by
_____.

* * *

5. Olivia in *So Evil My Love* was played by _____.

* * *

6. Gregory in *Gaslight* was played by _____.

* * *

7. Franz in *The Stranger* was played by _____.

* * *

8. Ellen in *Ladies in Retirement* was played by
_____.

* * *

9. Mundsen in *Gilda* was played by _____.

* * *

10. Jaffar in *The Thief of Bagdad* was played by _____.

† † †

18. WHERE DID THE TIME GO?

1. "The Star-Spangled Banner" was declared the national anthem in 1931. What was the name of the losing song?

* * *

2. The U.S. paid $25 million for a purchase from Denmark in 1917. What did we buy?

* * *

3. What was the first musical to win the Pulitzer Prize?

* * *

4. "In an Eighteenth Century Drawing Room" was written by a) Jimmie Van Heusen; b) Raymond Scott; c) Frank Loesser; or d) David Rose?

* * *

5. In 1938, newspapers reported that 25 bands played 5-¾ hours for 23,000 jitterbugs? Where did this occur?

* * *

6. The 1935 budget for WPA was a) $100 million; b) $500 million; c) $1 billion; or d) $5 billion?

* * *

7. What was the name of the U.S. gunboat sunk by the Japanese on the Yangtze in 1937?

* * *

8. What did Domino, Q.R.S., Black Swan, and Cameo have in common?

* * *

9. *Ceiling Zero, Captains of the Clouds,* and *Devil Dogs of the Air* all starred what actor?

† † †

19. FAMILY FILMING

Some Hollywood actors are second-generation stars. Name them and their talented parents:

1. The son was in *An American Tragedy;* the father was in *Ruggles of Red Gap.*

* * *

2. The son was in *Long Day's Journey into Night;* the father was in *Abraham Lincoln.*

* * *

3. The son was in *Psycho;* the father was in *Scarface.*

* * *

4. The son was in *The Cardinal;* the father was in *The Virginian.*

* * *

5. The son was in *Lilith;* the father was in *Jesse James.*

* * *

6. The son was in *The Victors;* the father was in *Crossfire.*

* * *

7. The son was in *Dead End;* the father was in *Abie's Irish Rose.*

*   *   *

8.   The son was in *Stage Coach;* the father was in *San Francisco.*

*   *   *

9.   The son was in *Tom Brown's School Days;* the father was in *The Scarlet Pimpernel.*

*   *   *

10.   The son was in *Born Yesterday;* the mother was in *Swing Time.*

20. GOOD RECEPTION

† † † † †

1. "Mr. Lincoln," by James Agee, featuring Royal Dano, was shown on what TV show?

* * *

2. Name the TV critic who hosted "Seven Lively Arts."

* * *

3. Bill Lundigan and Mary Costa hosted a) "Climax!"; b) "Playhouse 90"; c) "Matinee Theatre"; or d) "U.S. Steel Hour"?

* * *

4. The storyteller on "O. Henry Playhouse" was a) Leo G. Carroll; b) Walter Brennan; c) Thomas Mitchell; or d) Martin Balsam?

* * *

5. Name the original four partners who founded "Four Star Playhouse."

* * *

6. The teller of tales on "Teller of Tales" was a) Edgar Wallace; b) Somerset Maugham; c) Sax Rohmer; or d) Octavus Roy Cohen?

* * *

7. Name the judicious host on a) "Court of Last Resort"; b) "Justice"; c) "On Trial"; and d) "The Verdict Is Yours."

*   *   *

8. Name the medico-stars of a) "Dr. Hudson's Secret Journal"; b) "The Doctor"; c) "City Hospital"; and d) "Noah's Ark."

*   *   *

9. "Martin Kane" was played by a) Lee Tracy; b) Lloyd Nolan; c) William Gargan; or d) Mark Stevens?

*   *   *

10. Ellery Queen was played by a) Lee Bowman; b) Hugh Marlowe; c) George Nader; or d) Lee Phillips?

21. THE HISSABLES

1. He challenged James Dean to a game of "chicken" in *Rebel without a Cause.*

* * *

2. He tried to blackmail Dana Andrews into prosecuting Arthur Kennedy in *Boomerang.*

* * *

3. He killed Linda Darnell, then set about solving her murder, in *Fallen Angel.*

* * *

4. He was Major Salinas and persecuted Rory Calhoun in *Way of a Gaucho.*

* * *

5. He beat Frank Sinatra to death in *From Here to Eternity.*

* * *

6. He killed his wife and chopped up her body in *Rear Window.*

* * *

7. He was the vicious killer for whom Gary Cooper was mistaken in *Along Came Jones.*

*   *   *

8. He was Leroy, the insane janitor, in *The Bad Seed.*

*   *   *

9. He threw boiling coffee in Gloria Grahame's face in *The Big Heat.*

*   *   *

10. He masterminded the Nazi gang in *The Fallen Sparrow.*

22. BRING BACK BROADWAY

† † † † †

Match the stars with their shows:

1. Libby Holman, Lupe Velez, Paul and Grace Hartmann, and Clifton Webb
2. Dennis King, Vivienne Siegal, Walter Slezak, and Vera Zorina
3. Mitzi Green, Ray Heatherton, Robert Rounseville, and Alfred Drake
4. Albert Dekker, Lee J. Cobb, Elia Kazan, Luther Adler, John Garfield, and Morris Carnovsky
5. Fannie Brice, Bob Hope, Gertrude Niesen, Eve Arden, Judy Canova, June Preisser, and Josephine Baker
6. Ray Bolger, Monty Woolley, Luella Gear
7. Rudy Vallee, Bert Lahr, Willie and Eugene Howard, and Cliff Edwards
8. Beatrice Lilly, Reginald Gardiner, Eleanor Powell, Ethel Waters, Paul Haakon, and Vera-Ellen
9. Fannie Brice, Willie and Eugene Howard, Jane Froman, Buddy Ebsen, Eve Arden, June Preisser, Robert Cummings, and Ina Ray Hutton
10. Imogene Coca, Danny Kaye, Alfred Drake, Mata and Hari, and Jerome Robbins

a) *At Home Abroad*
b) *Johnny Johnson*
c) *The Straw Hat Revue*
d) *You Never Know*
e) *Ziegfeld Follies of 1934*

g) *Ziegfeld Follies* (1936)
h) *Babes in Arms*
i) *I Married an Angel*
j) *George White's Scandals*
k) *On Your Toes*

† † †

23. EVERYBODY, DANCE!

✝   ✝   ✝   ✝   ✝

Match the dancing picture and the stars:

1. *Dance, Girl, Dance*   a) Clara Bow and Alice Joyce
2. *Dance, Fools, Dance*   b) Joan Crawford and Franchot Tone
3. *Dancing in the Dark*   c) Cesar Romero and Carole Landis
4. *Dancing Lady*   d) Abbott and Costello
5. *Dance with Me, Henry*   e) Maureen O'Hara and Louis Hayward
6. *The Dancing Masters*   f) Joan Crawford and Clark Gable
7. *Dancing Mothers*   g) William Powell and Betsy Drake
8. *Dance Hall*   h) Laurel and Hardy

✝   ✝   ✝

40

24.   TIME TO PLAY BALL

1. Who was the youngest manager of an AL team?

*   *   *

2. On May 30, 1927, shortstop Jim Cooney for the Chicago Cubs made an unassisted triple play against the Pittsburgh Pirates. When was the next time this occurred?

*   *   *

3. Pepper, Dizzy, Rip, and Lippy were part of the Gashouse Gang. What were their last names?

*   *   *

4. Why did Happy Chandler threaten to ban dozens of ballplayers in 1946?

*   *   *

5. Who was John A. Heydler?

*   *   *

6. In 1950, a Phillie player, son of a famous first baseman, hit a tenth-inning homer on the last day of the season to help his team grab their first pennant in 35 years. Who was he, and what was his father's name?

*   *   *

7. Who was the pitcher who gave Bobby Thomson his famous home run in the 1951 National League playoff between New York and Brooklyn?

*   *   *

8. The Yankees paid $20,000 for an outfielder in 1937. What was his name?

*   *   *

9. Who won their only American League pennant in 1944?

*   *   *

10. Which American League team won 111 games in one season?

†   †   †

25. SCAREY PIX

1. *Frankenstein* was directed by a) James Whale; b) Tod Browning; c) Robert Florey; or d) Michael Curtiz?

* * *

2. The count in *The Most Dangerous Game* was played by a) Joel McCrea; b) Leslie Banks; or c) Robert Armstrong?

* * *

3. Arisztid Olt's movie name was a) Peter Lorre; b) Bela Lugosi; c) Rondo Hatton; or d) Olga Baclanova?

* * *

4. Bela Lugosi took over the vampire chores in *Dracula* from whom?

* * *

5. Who played the Wolfman in *The Werewolf of London?*

* * *

6. Who played the Ape Man in *Dr. Renault's Secret?*

* * *

7. Who played the lady vampire in *Mark of the Vampire:* a) Gloria Stuart; b) Carol Borland; c) Jacqueline Wells; or d) Veda Ann Borg?

*   *   *

8. Dr. Cyclops was played by a) Thomas Coley; b) Victor Kilian; or c) Albert Dekker?

*   *   *

9. *Cat People* was directed by a) Jacques Tourneur; b) A. E. Sutherland; or c) Robert Siodmak?

*   *   *

10. *The Leopard Man* was produced by a) Charles Brackett; b) Val Lewton; or c) Rowland V. Lee?

†   †   †

26. TRUMPET TRIVIA

How many trumpet players can you identify?

1. Led the Original Memphis Five.
2. Sang and played trumpet on Artie Shaw's "Blues in the Night" recording.
3. Married singer Keely Smith.
4. Famous for his "wa wa" effects on early Duke Ellington records.
5. Left Duke Ellington in 1940 for Benny Goodman, and Raymond Scott wrote a tune in honor of the occasion.
6. Wrote "Undecided."
7. Recorded "Let Me Off Uptown" with Anita O'Day and Gene Krupa.
8. Plays the fluegelhorn.
9. Played at Nick's and Eddie Condon's.

    a) Cootie Williams
    b) Louis Prima
    c) Charlie Shavers
    d) Wild Bill Davison
    e) Roy Eldridge
    f) Bugger Miley
    g) Hot Lips Page
    h) Phil Napoleon
    i) Miles Davis

27. ANNA'S IN THE MOVIES

† † † † †

Match the clue with the movie:

1. Silvana Mangano as a sultry convent-bound girl. (Remember the mambo?)
2. Siam and Wales, Rex as the Rex, Irene as the missionary.
3. "Vhisky, please."
4. A Tolstoy plot.
5. A kittenish film, starring the feline Eartha.
6. A wonderful weeper, with Anne Shirley.
7. Jacques Tourneur directed this adventure film. Louis Jourdan and Jean Peters were his stars.
8. Here comes Anne Shirley again, with James Ellison by her side.
9. The singing story of a gal, her gun, and her guy.
10. Number 9, sans songs.

  a) *Anne of Windy Poplars*
  b) *Annie Oakley*
  c) *Anna*
  d) *Anne of Green Gables*
  e) *Anne of the Indies*
  f) *Anna Christie*
  g) *Annie Get Your Gun*
  h) *Anna Lucasta*
  i) *Anna Karenina*
  j) *Anna and the King of Siam*

† † †

28. EGO BOOSTING

Match the autobiography with its author:

1. *Steps in Time*
2. *Too Much, Too Soon*
3. *With a Feather on My Nose*
4. *Laughter Is a Wonderful Thing*
5. *A Smattering of Ignorance*
6. *The Man in the Straw Hat*
7. *My Life in Your Hands*
8. *Wayfaring Stranger*
9. *The Big Cage*
10. *Call Me Lucky*

a) Diane Barrymore
b) Bing Crosby
c) Billie Burke
d) Maurice Chevalier
e) Oscar Levant
f) Eddie Cantor
g) Burl Ives
h) Clyde Beatty
i) Joe E. Brown
j) Fred Astaire

29. SEEING DOUBLE

† † † † †

Match the clue with the film:

1. Peter Lorre appeared in this British-made film about vacations at a seaside resort.
2. Donald O'Connor and Hope Emerson were in this takeoff of thud-and-blunder sword-and-dagger movies.
3. Even with Frank Sinatra and Groucho Marx, this movie was a fraction of what it should have been.
4. Billy Wilder directed this classic of an insurance man who tried to cash in on a policy.
5. Ronald Colman couldn't make up his mind who he was.
6. Bing Crosby and Martha Raye in a get-rich-quick scheme.
7. William Powell and Myrna Loy—but not a *Thin Man* movie. He was a painter, she was a dress designer.
8. Harry Langdon, Buddy Rogers, and a lot of beans.
9. Danny Kaye played a GI and a British general.
10. An ancestor of *Blow Up*. Nancy Kelly was a girl photographer who accidentally takes a picture of a murder.

a) *Double or Nothing* f) *Double Dynamite*
b) *Double Crossbones* g) *Double Indemnity*
c) *Double Trouble* h) *A Double Life*
d) *Double Exposure* i) *Double Wedding*
e) *Double Confession* j) *On the Double*

† † †

48

30. YEAR: 1931

1. In 1931, a Marine Corps general accused a foreign ruler of running over a child. Name the leatherneck and the foreign ruler.

* * *

2. The 1931 Nobel Peace Prize was shared by the president of Columbia University and the founder of Hull House. Their names?

* * *

3. Who was the minister who dedicated the Riverside Church in New York, in 1931?

* * *

4. At a writers dinner in 1931, the author of *An American Tragedy* slapped the author of *Main Street* across the face. Name the battling writers.

* * *

5. Who was named, in 1931, to head the world's tallest building?

* * *

6. Who were the Scottsboro boys?

* * *

7. Who was the beloved sports figure killed in a 1931 airplane crash, near Bazaar, Kansas?

8. A tiny French coloratura soprano appeared in 1931 at the Metropolitan Opera House, singing *Lucia di Lammermoor.* Her name?

9. Radio Station HVJ was dedicated in 1931, and a world figure made the opening speech. Where was HVJ and who made the dedication?

10. Name the second baseman of the St. Louis Cardinals who set a record in 1931 when he hit three homers in one game.

31. GREAT MOVIE LINES

† † † † †

Where do these movie quotes come from?

1. "The fog . . . for a while you can't see where you're going . . . then it lifts." a) *Anna Karenina;* b) *Anna Christie;* c) *Flesh and the Devil*

* * *

2. "I ate a butterfly once. Its wings tasted all dusty." a) *The Strange Love of Molly Louvain;* b) *A Free Soul;* c) *The Devil Is a Sissy*

* * *

3. "Of all the idiots in the diplomatic service, you are the worst." a) *Design for Living;* b) *The Merry Widow;* c) *One Hour with You*

* * *

4. "Why do I always get the girls who look like fire-horses?" a) *They Won't Forget;* b) *Kid Galahad;* c) *Two Seconds*

* * *

5. "Have you ever, of all the men you have known, seen such an Adonis?" a) *Mad Love;* b) *Kongo;* c) *The Florentine Dagger*

* * *

6. "I'm one of the nameless legion that always get stuck." a) *Dawn Patrol;* b) *Viva Villa!;* c) *The General Died at Dawn*

7. "I always was a whisky man myself, funny I should die for a drink of water." a) *The Prisoner of Shark Island;* b) *Drums Along the Mohawk;* c) *Billy the Kid*

* * *

8. "I want this moment to last . . . at least until breakfast." a) *Tonight Is Ours;* b) *Of Human Bondage;* c) *Twentieth Century*

* * *

9. "Never trust or love anyone so much you can't betray him." a) *Now, Voyager;* b) *The Prince and the Pauper;* c) *Flamingo Road*

* * *

10. "You have the touch of a sex-starved cobra." a) *The Man Who Came to Dinner;* b) *Torrid Zone;* c) *Hard to Handle*

† † †

32. VIDEO MEMORIES

1. The host of "Name That Tune" was a) George deWitt; b) Ralph Edwards; c) Bill Cullen; or d) Red Benson?

* * *

2. What were the areas of expertise for each of the following quiz-show contestants: a) Gino Prato ("$64,-000 Question"); b) Myrt Power ("$64,000 Challenge"); c) Billy Pearson ("$64,000 Challenge"); d) Redmond O'Hanlon ("$64,000 Challenge")?

* * *

3. "Will it be a hit or a miss?" asked Peter Potter on what show?

* * *

4. Moss Hart hosted what early TV quiz?

* * *

5. John Cameron Swayze and Robert Trout shared hosting honors on what early TV quiz?

* * *

6. Conrad Nagel hosted a) "The Name's the Same"; b) "It's News to Me"; c) "Who's Whose?"; or d) "Celebrity Time"?

* * *

7. What was the name of Fred Allen's quiz show?

8. Name the soap operas on which the following characters appeared: a) The Barron family; b) Laif and Millie Flaigle; c) Helen Emerson.

9. What do all these people have in common: George Cleveland, Tommy Rettig, Jan Clayton, Jon Provost, Cloris Leachman, and June Lockhart?

10. Peter Graves starred in what TV series about a boy and a horse?

33. WILDER CHARACTERS

† † † † †

Match the characters and the Billy Wilder film in which they appeared:

1. Susan Applegate, Major Kirby, Pamela Hill, and Mr. Osborn
2. Bramble, Mouche, Farid, and General Sebastiano
3. Walter Neff, Phyllis Dietrichson, and Barton Keys
4. Don Birnam, Helen St. James, Nat, and Wick
5. Virgil Smith, Johanna, Holenia, and Bitotska
6. Phoebe Frost, Erika von Schletow, Capt. John Pringle, and Col. Rufus Pluma
7. Norma Desmond, Jose Gillis, and Max von Mayerling
8. Charles Tatum, Lorraine, and Herbie Cook
9. Sefton, Dunbar, Stosh, and Harry
10. Flannagan, Ariane Chevasse, and Claude Chevasse
11. Leonard and Christine Vole, Sir Wilfrid Robars, and Miss Plimsoll
12. Sugar Kane, Joe, Jerry, Spats Columbo, and Osgood Fielding
13. C. C. Baxter, Fran Kubelik, and J. D. Sheldrake

a) *Love in the Afternoon*
b) *Sunset Boulevard*
c) *The Big Carnival*
d) *Double Indemnity*
e) *The Apartment*
f) *Some Like It Hot*
g) *Witness for the Prosecution*
h) *The Lost World*
i) *The Emperor Waltz*
j) *The Major and the Minor*
k) *A Foreign Affair*
l) *Five Graves to Cairo*
m) *Stalag 17*

† † †

34. WHO'S ON FIRST?

† † † † †

Match the ballplayer with his nickname:

1. John Joseph Murphy   a) Watty
2. Talmadge Lafayette Abernathy b) Grandma
3. Lambert Dalton Meyer   c) Luke
4. Lucius Benjamin Appling   d) Dutch
5. Albert Wayne Hollingsworth   e) Kiddo
6. William Watson Clark   f) Bump
7. Irving Darius Hadley   g) Sparky
8. George Willis Davis   h) Monk
9. Walter John Dubiel   i) Ted
10. Earl John Adams   j) Boots

† † †

35. MOVIE CLUES

† † † † †

Match the movie detective with the clue:

1. Inspector Faraday opposed Bert Lytell, Lionel Barrymore, William Russell, and Chester Morris. What character did all these men play?
2. Preston Foster played this private eye in *The Westland Case, Lady in the Morgue,* and *The Last Warning.*
3. This jewel thief was played by Bert Lytell, Henry B. Walthall, Jack Holt, Melvyn Douglas, Francis Lederer, and Warren William.
4. James Gleason played Inspector Oscar Piper opposite Edna May Oliver. Later, Helen Broderick and ZaSu Pitts also played this schoolteacher detective.
5. Joan Bennett, Loretta Young, and Heather Angel played Phyllis, opposite such actors as Jack Buchanan, Ralph Richardson, Ronald Colman, Kenneth McKenna, and Ray Milland.
6. Biff Elliot was the shamus; Preston Foster was the cop.
7. This serialized criminologist was played by Arnold Daly, Herbert Rawlinson, and Jack Mulhall.
8. Buster Crabbe played this detective in a Chinatown setting.
9. Victor Jory played three roles in this popular serial.
10. Ricardo Cortez nailed Bebe Daniels, who played the murderess in the first *The Maltese Falcon.*
11. This detective was played by both Boris Karloff and Keye Luke.

a) Red Barry
b) Hildegarde Withers
c) Bill Crane
d) Mike Hammer
e) Prof. Craig Kennedy
f) Bulldog Drummond
g) Boston Blackie
h) Sam Spade
i) The Shadow
j) Mr. Wong
k) The Lone Wolf

36. GOOD SOUNDS

† † † † †

Name their instrument:

1. Kid Ory, Jack Teagarden, J. J. Johnson, Miff Mole.
   _____

*   *   *

2. Benny Carter, Charlie Parker, Johnny Hodges.
   _____

*   *   *

3. Stan Getz, Bud Freeman, Lester Young, Sonny Rollins. _____

*   *   *

4. Buddy de Franco, Pee Wee Russell, Johnny Dodds.
   _____

*   *   *

5. Art Tatum, Teddy Wilson, Bud Powell, Count Basie. _____

*   *   *

6. Charlie Christian, Django Reinhardt, Eddie Lang, Barney Kessel. _____

*   *   *

7. Cozy Cole, Art Blakey, Buddy Rich, Dave Tough, Chick Webb. _____

*   *   *

8.   John Kirby, Oscar Pettiford, Jimmy Blanton. ____

*   *   *

9.   Stephane Grappelly, Joe Venuti, Stuff Smith. ____

*   *   *

10.   Sidney Bechet _____
       Gerry Mulligan _____
       Adrian Rollini _____

†   †   †

37.   1932 PERSONALITIES

Identify these 1932 people:

1.   The first woman to be elected to the U.S. Senate

*   *   *

2.   A wrestler whose real name was Christopher Theophilus

*   *   *

3.   Wang Lung and O-Lan

*   *   *

4.   Ellsworth Vines, Jr.

*   *   *

5.   The Tune Detective and the Song Sleuth

*   *   *

6.   Auguste Piccard

*   *   *

7.   William Beebe

*   *   *

8.   Mrs. George Palmer Putnam

*   *   *

9.   Grant Wood

*   *   *

10.   Ned Darrell and Nina Leeds

38.   '38 TO THE BAR

† † † † †

Match the instrument, the instrumentalist, and the 1938 band:

1. Charlie Spivak	a) trumpet	I. Count Basie
2. Frank De Vol	b) drums	II. Horace Heidt
3. Hal McIntyre	c) trombone	III. Larry Clinton
4. Jack Washington	d) sax	IV. Paul Whiteman
5. Hugo Winterhalter	e) clarinet	V. Benny Goodman
6. Yank Lausen	f) guitar	VI. Jimmy Dorsey
7. Charlie Teagarden		VII. Tommy Dorsey
8. Ray Conniff		VIII. Glenn Miller
9. Red Ballard		IX. Bunny Berigan
10. Alvino Rey		
11. Ray McKinley		

† † †

39. BLACK AND WHITE MOVIES

Match the clue and the movie:

1. Girl loves horse, horse loves girl.
2. Louis Hayward loves Janet Blair, George Macready hates both.
3. Karloff hates Lugosi, loves Satan.
4. Bogart hates foreigners.
5. Kay Francis loves nursing.
6. Walter Pidgeon loves Tonelayo.
7. James Cagney loves his mom.
8. Ian Keith hates mosquitos.
9. Carole Lombard hates Charles Laughton.
10. Robert Frazer loves a gorilla.

    a) *The Black Cat*
    b) *White Heat*
    c) *Black Beauty*
    d) *White Legion*
    e) *Black Legion*
    f) *The White Angel*
    g) *The Black Arrow*
    h) *White Woman*
    i) *White Zombie*
    j) *White Cargo*

40. YEARBOOKS

1. In 1939 Grace Zaring Stone wrote a pseudonymous bestseller about Nazi Germany. What were her nom de plume and the book's title?

*   *   *

2. A novel originally written in Yiddish about the New Testament hit the 1939 bestseller lists. Who was the author, and what was the book?

*   *   *

3. An author who became a frequent guest on "Information, Please" wrote a 1940 bestseller about England. Who was she, and what was her book?

*   *   *

4. Who was the woman explorer whose story about her adventures sold over 285,000 copies in 1940? What was her book?

*   *   *

5. What was the book of poetry by Alice Duer Miller that sold 250,000 copies in the early forties and was later made into both a movie and a song?

*   *   *

6. Alma Gluck's daughter wrote a 1943 bestseller about a Pennsylvania mine-owning family. Who was she, and what was the book?

7. Who was the author and what bestselling historical novel of hers won MGM's $125,000 prize in 1944?

* * *

8. Boston banned two books in 1944. One of them was *Forever Amber.* What was the other?

* * *

9. Name the war correspondent whose book, *The Curtain Rises,* was a bestseller in 1944.

* * *

10. Who wrote the exposé of subversive activities, *Under Cover,* which was a 1944 bestseller?

† † †

41. HOLLYWOOD HOME TEAM

Match the baseball movie and the star:

 1. *Alibi Ike*   a) Edward G. Robinson
 2. *Death on the Diamond*   b) Ronald Reagan
 3. *Swell-Head*   c) Ray Milland
 4. *Ladies' Day*   d) Robert Young
 5. *The Heckler*   e) Dan Dailey
 6. *It Happens Every Spring*   f) Wallace Ford
 7. *The Big Leaguer*   g) Eddie Albert
 8. *The Pride of St Louis*   h) Charlie Chase
 9. *The Winning Team*   i) William Bendix
10. *Kill the Umpire*   j) Joe E. Brown

42.   NEWSMAKERS

1.   Who was Joseph Zangara?

*   *   *

2.   What was the *Amberjack II*?

*   *   *

3.   Who was Nellie Taylor Ross?

*   *   *

4.   Who headed Commonwealth & Southern, the anti-TVA utility?

*   *   *

5.   What did all these people have in common: Charles Boettcher II, John Factor, Charles F. Urschel, John O'Connell, Peggy McMarth, Mary McElroy, and William Hamm?

*   *   *

6.   What did Washington's false teeth, Sally Rand, and the Sky Ride have in common?

*   *   *

7.   Rear Admiral W. A. Moffett was drowned in what 1933 tragedy?

*   *   *

8.   Who completed a 29,000-mile flight for Pan American in 1933?

*   *   *

9.   In what year was the Baseball All-Star game born?

*   *   *

10.   What movie director wrote *Damien the Leper*?

43. BIG MOVIES

† † † † †

Match the clue with the movie:

1. George Burns's radio station is saved by the Old Groaner.
2. Aboard the S. S. *Art Deco,* Kirsten Flagstad sings Wagner, and Bob sings "Thanks for the Memory."
3. A bitter Billy Wilder picture, with Kirk Douglas as a reporter on the make.
4. The excitement meter keeps running in this Spencer Tracy–Luise Rainer movie.
5. Rube Eric Linden trips over love.
6. Victor McLaglen, one hand on the electric-chair switch, is tempted.
7. Stone walls do a good movie make, when Wallace Beery, Chester Morris, and Robert Montgomery are in it.
8. Bogart and Bacall and their patented brand of electricity.
9. Would Macy's tell Gimbels? Not in this Marx Brothers movie.
10. Crime's only skin deep in this Bette Davis and Ricardo Cortez mellerdrama.

a) *The Big Guy*
b) *Big City Blues*
c) *The Big Broadcast*
d) *The Big Store*
e) *The Big Sleep*
f) *The Big Broadcast of 1938*
g) *The Big Carnival*
h) *The Big House*
i) *The Big Shakedown*
j) *Big City*

† † †

44. BANDSTAND

1. This trumpet player was married to Mamie Van Doren. His biggest hit was "Dragnet."

* * *

2. This singer's first record was "What Kind o' Man Is You," recorded with Ed Lang's orchestra. She was Whiteman's vocalist for several years.

* * *

3. This singer starred in *St. Louis Blues.* She was a band vocalist with Cootie Williams.

* * *

4. She was known as the "Tweedle Dee Girl."

* * *

5. This guitarist was once married to Peggy Lee.

* * *

6. This saxaphonist's biggest record was "Cherokee."

* * *

7. This orchestra leader studied organ with Fats Waller.

* * *

8. His most famous record, "Singin' the Blues," influenced a whole generation of horn players.

9.   Born in 1883, this long-lived pianist's hits include his own composition, "I'm Just Wild about Harry."

*   *   *

10.   This pianist not only worked with Tommy Dorsey, Benny Goodman, and Louis Armstrong—he appeared in a Broadway production, *Rat Race.*

†   †   †

45. ADVENTURE MOVIES

† † † † †

Match the clue and the movie:

1. This adolescent Shirley Temple picture was set at the turn of the century.
2. Yes, Gable's back and Garson's got him.
3. Jean Arthur and Joel McCrea starred in this offbeat bank-robbery comedy.
4. Herbert Marshall and Virginia Bruce up to their well-bred eyebrows in juvenile delinquency.
5. Gary Cooper in a Far Easterner, with Lana Turner as one of the handmaidens.
6. The boys at Locksley Hall.
7. Victor Jory and Walter Brennan in a Mark Twain classic.
8. Clue: Mrs. Hudson is the landlady.
9. Is that Perry Mason/Ironside with Errol Flynn?

   a) *Adventure in Manhattan*
   b) *The Adventures of Tom Sawyer*
   c) *Adventure in Baltimore*
   d) *Adventure*
   e) *Adventures of Sherlock Holmes*
   f) *Adventures of Robin Hood*
   g) *The Adventures of Marco Polo*
   h) *Adventure in Washington*
   i) *Adventures of Don Juan*

† † †

46. UNCLASSIFIED CLASSICS

1. Who wrote *Bad Girl, Loose Ladies, Kept Women,* and *The Marriage Racket?*

* * *

2. Bob, Jerry, Ned, Professor Snodgrass, and Noddy Nixon appeared in what series?

* * *

3. Ruth and Alice De Vere appeared in what series?

* * *

4. Freddie, Bert, Nan and Flossie, and Dinah appeared in what series?

* * *

5. Bob Burke, Jack Curtis, Hank Handcraft, and Bill Bender appeared in what series?

* * *

6. Andy Foger, Mary Nestor, Ned Newton, and Wakefield appeared in what series?

* * *

7. Joe, Frank, Chet Morton, Sam Hadley, and Callie Shaw appeared in what series?

* * *

8. Muckluck Mag, Windy Ike, and Sailor Swede were creations of what poet?

* * *

9. "Let Me Live in a House by the Side of the Road, and Be a Friend to Man" was written by a) Joyce Kilmer; b) Berton Braley; c) Sam Walter Foss; or d) Edgar Guest?

* * *

10. The *Shorty Masters* pulp western series was written by a) Allan Bosworth; b) W. Bert Foster; c) Ray Nafzier; or d) Luke Short?

47. THEY'RE ALL MOVIES

✝   ✝   ✝   ✝   ✝

Match the clue with the movie:

1. Curtain going up on this behind-the-scenes movie, with Bette Davis, Anne Baxter, Celeste Holm . . . and Marilyn Monroe.
2. An Arthur Miller work, with Edward G. Robinson and Burt Lancaster.
3. Fredric March as a professor and Helen Mack as a gun moll.
4. Peace in our time.
5. The father of John as the Father of Lies.
6. Broderick Crawford as a southern emperor.
7. Anatole Litvak directed, Rachel Field wrote the book, Charles Boyer and Bette Davis starred.
8. Humphrey Bogart encounters the Nazis.
9. Barbara Stanwyck strays—temporarily—from the path of virtue.
10. Not *On the Town* or *Anchors Aweigh,* even though it's about three gobs on shore leave.
   - a) *All Quiet on the Western Front*
   - b) *All Ashore*
   - c) *All through the Night*
   - d) *All I Desire*
   - e) *All My Sons*
   - f) *All of Me*
   - g) *All About Eve*
   - h) *All That Money Can Buy*
   - i) *All This and Heaven, Too*
   - j) *All the King's Men*

48. THE GREAT ENGINEER'S TEAM

† † † † †

Who filled these posts in Herbert Hoover's cabinet?

1. Vice President
2. Secretary of State
3. Secretary of Treasury
4. Secretary of War
5. Attorney General
6. Postmaster General
7. Secretary of the Navy
8. Secretary of the Interior
9. Secretary of Agriculture
10. Secretary of Commerce
11. Secretary of Labor

a) James DeWitt Mitchell
b) Charles F. Adams
c) Henry L. Stimson
d) Walter F. Brown
e) Charles Curtis
f) Ray L. Wilbur
g) Arthur M. Hyde
h) Roy D. Chapin
i) William N. Doak
j) Andrew W. Mellon
k) Patrick J. Hurley

† † †

49. RKO SAHARA

1. Ruth Roman and Akim Tamiroff appeared in this dry film.

* * *

2. Can you name both pictures in which James Mason appeared as Field Marshal Ernst Rommel?

* * *

3. Burt Lancaster, Mary Astor, Lizabeth Scott, and Wendell Corey were in this furious movie.

* * *

4. Yvonne De Carlo, Rock Hudson . . . and Jackie Gleason were seen in this film.

* * *

5. Here comes the Legion, with such stalwarts as Brian Keith, Richard Denning, and Johnny Desmond.

* * *

6. Courage, mon braves—another Legion epic. This time with Alan Ladd, Richard Conte, Akim Tamiroff and . . . Arlene Dahl.

* * *

7. Stiff upper lip, lads. Richard Attenborough, John Gregson, and Michael Craig try to blow up a German fuel supply.

* * *

8. Can you name two songs from *The Desert Song?*

* * *

9. Stan and Ollie were conventioneers in this comedy.

* * *

10. This camel-and-fig fable starred Ralph Meeker and J. Carrol Naish.

† † †

50. AERO-RADIO

1. Whose "Air Adventures" were broadcast weekly?

* * *

2. What was the name of Ivan Shark's daughter on "Captain Midnight"?

* * *

3. Name the radio program dedicated to Coast Guard aviators.

* * *

4. Chester Stratton starred as whom?

* * *

5. What show had such characters as Donna Cavendish, Burton York, Zero Smith, and The Chief?

* * *

6. Who belonged to the AAF?

* * *

7. Penny and Clipper were characters on what show?

* * *

8. What was the show based on Zack Mosley's comic strip?

*   *   *

9. What was the Sparrow and the Hawk's family name?

*   *   *

10. Who sponsored "Wings of Destiny"?

†   †   †

51.   CASTING CALL

Match the actors with the movies:

1. Buster Crabbe, El Brendel, Victor Jory
2. Peggy Wood, Olivia De Havilland, Roland Young
3. Bob Hope, Anita Ekberg, Edie Adams
4. Ethel Merman
5. Dan Dailey and Betty Grable
6. Jimmy Stewart
7. Jack Oakie, Clark Gable, Loretta Young
8. Lon Chaney, Jr.

9. Richard Arlen
10. Walter Pidgeon

a) *Call of the Wild*
b) *Calling Dr. Death*
c) *Calling Bulldog Drummond*
d) *Call a Messenger*
e) *The Calling of Dan Matthews*
f) *Call It a Day*
g) *Call Me Madam*
h) *Call Northside 777*
i) *Call Me Mister*
j) *Call Me Bwana*

52. AND NOW A WORD FROM . . .

† † † † †

Match the sponsor and the radio show:

1. International Sterling
2. Lipton Tea
3. Dr. Lyons Tooth Powder
4. Alka Seltzer
5. Eversharp
6. Raleigh Pipe Tobacco
7. Campbell Soup
8. Spic and Span
9. Rinso
10. Feen-a-Mint

a) "Life Can Be Beautiful"
b) "The Curt Massey and Martha Tilton Show"
c) "Big Sister"
d) "The Adventures of Ozzie and Harriet"
e) "Arthur Godfrey's Talent Scouts"
f) "Double or Nothing"
g) "Uncle Walter's Dog House"
h) "Amos 'n' Andy"
i) "Manhattan Merry Go Round"
j) "Take It or Leave It"

† † †

53.   FOLLOW THE STAR

(Each question is a clue to this actress's identity.)

1. She was born in Oklahoma City in 1906, the daughter of vaudevillian Katherine Clinton.

*   *   *

2. In *The Cocoanuts* she was outwitted by the Marx Brothers.

*   *   *

3. She appeared opposite William Powell in *Street of Chance.*

*   *   *

4. She appeared with Walter Huston and Kenneth MacKenna in *Virtuous Sin.*

*   *   *

5. Lionel Barrymore was the murderer, but she was the accused in *Guilty Hands.*

*   *   *

6. She also appeared in Tay Garnett's *One Way Passage.*

*   *   *

7. Bebe Daniels got the part she was meant for in *42d Street.*

* * *

8. She appeared with Edward G. Robinson in *I Loved a Woman.*

* * *

9. Her part in *Wonder Bar* was cut to give more room to Dolores Del Rio.

* * *

10. In *Charley's Aunt,* she was the aunt.

† † †

54. BIG LEAGUE PLAYOFF

† † † † †

Match the 1939 American League clubs with their managers, and the managers' names with their first or nicknames:

1. New York	a)	Joe	I.	Baker	
2. Boston	b)	Pudge	II.	McCarthy	
3. Cleveland	c)	Bucky	III.	Haney	
4. Chicago	d)	Jimmie	IV.	Vitt	
5. Detroit	e)	Delmer	V.	Cronin	
6. Washington	f)	Oscar	VI.	Mack	
7. Philadelphia	g)	Marse Joe	VII.	Dykes	
8. St. Louis	h)	Connie	VIII.	Harris	

† † †

55. RING THE BELL

† † † † †

Match the clue with the movie:

1. John Hodiak was an Army officer, William Bendix his aide, and Gene Tierney played a blond Italian.
2. Fred Astaire danced with Vera Ellen, but Alice Pearce stole the show.
3. Leo McCarey directed this Mae West pic.
4. Gypsy Rose Lee staying clad; Randolph Scott going to good from bad; Dinah Shore looking sad.
5. Father Bing and Sister Ingrid.
6. "The Party's Over" and "Just in Time" were two of the songs in this Judy Holliday movie.
7. Myrna Loy lectures in this sequel to *Cheaper by the Dozen.*
8. British, but no stiff upper lips in a roaring comedy.
9. Gene Tierney, without a hair out of place, shoots 'em up.
10. Vera Hruba Ralston vies with John Carroll for the bland sweepstakes.

    a) *Belle Starr*
    b) *Belle of the Nineties*
    c) *The Belles of St. Trinian's*
    d) *A Bell for Adano*
    e) *Belle le Grand*
    f) *The Belle of New York*
    g) *Belles on Their Toes*
    h) *Belle of the Yukon*
    i) *Bells Are Ringing*
    j) *The Bells of St Mary's*

† † †

56. REMEMBER THESE IVORY-TICKLERS?

Match the pianist and the clue:

1. Composed "Misty."
2. His bands employed such greats as Joe Venuti, Eddie Lang, and the Dorsey brothers.
3. He worked with Benny Goodman as pianist, singer, and arranger.
4. Wrote "Tenderly."
5. First jazz musician to solo on the harpsichord, on a Gramercy Five recording.
6. He was once a professional prizefighter, later played with Fats Domino.
7. He was Bing Crosby's radio-show arranger in the early thirties, later married Lena Horne.
8. Started out as a chemist, later had his own group, with personnel such as Chu Berry, Louis Armstrong, John Kirby, and Coleman Hawkins.
9. His best-known tune is "Rosetta."
10. He claimed that he invented jazz in 1902.

a) Earl Hines
b) Screaming Jay Hawkins
c) Lennie Hayton
d) Jean Goldkette
e) Walter Gross

g) Fletcher Henderson
h) Jelly Roll Morton
i) Buddy Greco
j) Erroll Garner
k) Johnny Guarnieri

57. MADISON AVENUE ON THE AIR

† † † † †

Match the sponsor with the radio show:

1. Spry
2. Raleigh Pipe Tobacco
3. Kellogg's
4. Pall Mall
5. Welch's Grape Juice
6. Bristol Myers
7. Mars Bars
8. Philip Morris
9. Life Buoy
10. Thrivo
11. Camay

a) "The Ken Murray Program"
b) "Falstaff Fables"
c) "Duffy's Tavern"
d) "Dear John"
e) "The Big Story"
f) "The Singing Lady"
g) "Aunt Jenny"
h) "Beat the Band"
i) "The Moylan Sisters"
j) "Pepper Young's Family"
k) "It Pays to Be Ignorant"

† † †

58. BIG LEAGUE PLAYOFF # 2

Match the 1939 National League ball clubs with their managers, and the managers' last names with their first names:

1. Cincinnati	a) Doc	I. Traynor
2. St. Louis	b) Lippy	II. Prothro
3. Brooklyn	c) Casey	III. McKechnie
4. Chicago	d) Gabby	IV. Durocher
5. New York	e) Ray	V. Hartnett
6. Pittsburgh	f) Pie	VI. Terry
7. Boston	g) Bill	VII. Stengel
8. Philadelphia	h) Deacon	VIII. Blades

59. MEET ME AT THE MOVIES

† † † † †

Match the clue with the movie:

1. A screwball comedy with Charles Boyer, Margaret Sullavan, and Reginald Denny.
2. George Sanders goes on the radio for Germany, but who's his real sponsor?
3. Alan Ladd sees that the airmail gets through.
4. Elizabeth Taylor, Jane Powell, and Carmen Miranda, olé.
5. Dan Dailey sells Indian oil, courts Diana Lynn.
6. Judy Garland and Margaret O'Brien and an exposition.
7. Ex–Broadway biggie Lucille Ball tries to make a comeback. Dick Powell, Bert Lahr, and June Allyson help.
8. Capra-corn with Gary and Barbara.
9. Kindly old Jean Hersholt prescribes TLC.
10. You know this was made in 1952—both Sinatra and Shelley Winters are slim.

   a) *Meet Dr. Christian*
   b) *Appointment in Berlin*
   c) *Meet Me in St. Louis*
   d) *Meet Me at the Fair*
   e) *Appointment with Danger*
   f) *Meet Danny Wilson*
   g) *Meet the People*
   h) *Appointment for Love*
   i) *A Date with Judy*
   j) *Meet John Doe*

† † †

60. FAMILIAR VOICES

† † † † †

Match the announcer and the radio show:

1. Don Wilson
2. Ken Carpenter

3. Jimmy Wellington
4. Harry Von Zell
5. Bill Hay
6. Pierre Andre
7. Franklyn MacCormack
8. George Ansbro
9. Harlow Wilcox
10. Fred Foy

11. André Baruch
12. Dan Seymour

a) "Burns and Allen"
b) "Fibber McGee and Molly"
c) "Eddie Cantor"
d) "Aunt Jenny"
e) "Jack Benny"
f) "Kraft Music Hall"
g) "The Lone Ranger"
h) "Your Hit Parade"
i) "Amos 'n' Andy"
j) "Little Orphan Annie"
k) "Jack Armstrong"
l) "Young Widder Brown"

† † †

61.   BACK AGAIN

† † † † †

Match the clue with the movie:

1. Bill Mauldin's creations—Willie and Joe—in Tokyo.
2. Depression drabness with Van Heflin, Aline Mac-Mahon.
3. This Fannie Hurst love story was filmed three times, but Charles Boyer and Margaret Sullavan's version was probably the best.
4. John Wayne vs. the Emperor's sneaky forces.
5. A seasick Rock Hudson and Marcia Henderson vs. Steve Cochran.
6. Little Peter and fat Sidney with George Raft and Brenda Marshall.
7. Gordon MacRae, Dane Clark, and Ed Begley in a picnic of sordid types.
8. Chester Morris, Lucille Ball, and John Carradine discover themselves in the Amazon.
9. "Do I love Lucy?" asks George Brent. "You don't!" sues Miss Ball, fuming over Vera Zorina.
10. Gene, Champion, and Smiley have to deal with a copper boom.

a) *Back Street*
b) *Lover Come Back*
c) *Back to Bataan*
d) *Five Came Back*
e) *Back in God's Country*
f) *Back at the Front*
g) *Backfire*
h) *Back Door to Heaven*
i) *Back in the Saddle*
j) *Background to Danger*

† † †

62. "GEE, BOSS!"

† † † † †

Match the radio heroes and their sidekicks:

1. Nero Wolfe
2. The Bishop
3. Boston Blackie
4. Bulldog Drummond
5. Gregory Hood
6. Charlie Wild
7. The Cisco Kid
8. Count of Monte Cristo
9. David Harding
10. Jungle Jim
11. Ken Thurston
12. Martin Kane
13. Peter Quill
14. Mandrake
15. Bradley Drake

a) The Gargoyle
b) Pancho
c) Peters
d) Lothar
e) Archie Goodwin
f) Kolu
g) Denny
h) Happy McMann
i) McCoy
j) Rene
k) Sandy
l) Roger Dorn
m) Steve
n) Pagan Zeldschmidt
o) Shorty

† † †

63. FRANKENSTEIN'S OTHER FACES

Match Boris Karloff's role and the movie:

1. He is a baritone.
2. He is a Chinese bandit.
3. He is a Chinese detective.
4. He is an executioner.
5. He is a cancer researcher.
6. He is a German spy.
7. He is a professor with a split personality.
8. He is a Greek general.
9. He is an insane clothing designer.
10. He is an Indian chief.
11. He is a Scotland Yard official.

a) *Unconquered*
b) *Charlie Chan at the Opera*
c) *Isle of the Dead*
d) *Lured*
e) *Black Friday*
f) *War Lord*
g) *Tower of London*
h) *The Man With Nine Lives*
i) *Enemy Agent*
j) *Colonel March Investigates*
k) *The Mystery of Mr. Wong*

64. ALL BOOKED UP

1. Arthur Kallet and J. F. Schlink gave consumerism a headstart with their 1933 bestseller. Name it.

* * *

2. Alexander Woolcott recommended this book in 1934 as a book to "go quietly mad over," and made it a bestseller. What was its name, the author's name?

* * *

3. Who was the Smith College professor who wrote the 1934 bestseller, *Mary Peters?*

* * *

4. Peter Fleming, Ian's peripatetic brother, wrote a 1934 bestseller about his travels. Name it.

* * *

5. What was the religious book by Charles Dickens that became a surprise bestseller in 1934?

* * *

6. Who was the children's-book writer-illustrator who struck paydirt in 1935 with an adult novel, *Time out of Mind?*

* * *

7. Patience, Richard, and Johnny Abbe wrote a travel book that made the 1936 bestseller list. Name it.

*   *   *

8. Marjorie Hillis wrote two bestsellers—one right after the other. Name them.

*   *   *

9. Laura Krey's novel about Texas was a 1938 bestseller. Name it.

*   *   *

10. What was the 1938 inspirational bestseller by Lin Yutang, the Chinese scholar?

†   †   †

65. FANTASTIC RECALL

1. "There are some things man is not meant to know" was first uttered in a) *The Invisible Ray;* b) *The Hands of Orlac;* or c) *Dracula?*

* * *

2. The first future sequence of *Things to Come* is set in the year a) 1966; b) 1984; c) 2000; or d) 3540?

* * *

3. A lost civilization exists under Gene Autry's ranch in a) *The Phantom Empire;* b) *Undersea Kingdom;* or c) *King of the Rocket Men?*

* * *

4. The robot Maria in the German silent classic *Metropolis* was played by a) Gloria Holden; b) Brigitte Helm; c) Pola Negri; or d) Marlene Dietrich?

* * *

5. *Metropolis* was directed by a) Billy Wilder; b) Fritz Lang; or c) Kurt Siodmak?

* * *

6. Who has to steal living blood in order to live, in *The Return of Doctor X?* a) Clark Gable; b) Orson Welles; c) Humphrey Bogart; d) Joan Crawford; e) Hope Hampton

7.   Phylip Wylie was co-scenarist of a) *The Island of Lost Souls;* b) *Maytime;* c) *King Kong;* or d) *Gone with the Wind?*

* * *

8.   Lionel Atwill tried to cure Lon Chaney, Jr.'s lycanthropy by softening his brain in a) *House of Dracula;* b) *Donovan's Brain;* or c) *The Black Cat?*

* * *

9.   Erich von Stroheim played a mad doctor in a) *House of Dracula;* b) *Donovan's Brain;* or c) *The Black Cat?*

* * *

10.   John Barrymore was a mad doctor in a) *Donovan's Brain;* b) *The Island of Lost Souls;* c) *The Invisible Woman;* or d) *House of Dracula?*

* * *

11.   Richard Carlson's ancestor was a frog in what 3-D film: a) *Bwana Devil;* b) *House of Wax;* c) *The Maze;* or d) *Man in the Dark?*

† † †

66. FDR'S TEAM

Who filled these posts in FDR's cabinet?

1. Vice President
2. Secretary of State
3. Secretary of the Treasury
4. Secretary of War
5. Attorney General
6. Postmaster General
7. Secretary of the Navy
8. Secretary of the Interior

9. Secretary of Agriculture
10. Secretary of Commerce

11. Secretary of Labor

a) Daniel C. Roper
b) Harold L. Ickes
c) George H. Dern
d) Henry A. Wallace
e) John N. Garner
f) Frances Perkins
g) Cordell Hull
h) Homer S. Cummings
i) James A. Farley
j) Henry Morgenthau, Jr.
k) Claude A. Swanson

67.   FOLLOW THE STAR

(Each question is a clue to this actress's identity.)

1.   She was born in 1902, in Fort Sam Houston, Tex.

*   *   *

2.   In 1923 she starred in *Tarnish* on Broadway.

*   *   *

3.   Her first movie was *Paris Bound,* with Fredric March.

*   *   *

4.   She played opposite Ronald Colman in *Condemned.*

*   *   *

5.   She was a cockney governess in *Devotion.*

*   *   *

6.   In *Westward Passage* she played a divorcee.

*   *   *

7.   Leslie Howard preferred her to Myrna Loy in *The Animal Kingdom.*

*   *   *

8.   She played Gary Cooper's childhood love in *Peter Ibbetson.*

*   *   *

9. She played Walter Huston's wife in *Mission to Moscow*.

*   *   *

10. In *The Man in the Gray Flannel Suit* she was Frederic March's wife.

Her name:

†   †   †

68. RADIO REVERIES

Match the theme song and the radio show:

1. "Arthur Godfrey Time"
2. "The Judy Canova Show"
3. "Betty and Bob"
4. "John's Other Wife"
5. "The Fred Allen Show"
6. "Challenge of the Yukon"
7. "The Big Story"
8. "Hollywood Hotel"
9. "The Henry Morgan Show"

a) "Smile, Darn Ya, Smile"
b) "Salut d'Amour"
c) "Blue Moon"
d) "Seems Like Old Times"
e) "Goodnight, Sweetheart"
f) "The Sweetest Story Ever Told"
g) Overture to "Donna Diana"
h) "Ein Heldenleben"
i) "For He's a Jolly Good Fellow"

69.   BYGONE BESTSELLERS

1. A top fiction bestseller of 1930, about pioneer Oklahoma, was by an author whose previous bestseller had been in 1924. Name the author and both books.

*   *   *

2. What was the name of Thornton Wilder's story of classical Greece—a surprise bestseller of 1930?

*   *   *

3. This first novel by a Chicago writer won her the 1931 Pulitzer Prize. Name her and her book.

*   *   *

4. Some 20 years after her *Man in Lower Ten* had become the first American crime bestseller, this author hit the jackpot again in 1930. Name her and her book.

*   *   *

5. Galsworthy created the Forsythe family. But who created the Herries family?

*   *   *

6. 1930 saw the first medical bestseller. It was written by Dr. Axel Munthe. Remember its name?

*   *   *

7. In 1931, a member of Russia's royal family hit the bestseller list with her autobiography. Name her and her book.

8. An anonymous bestseller blew the lid off the nation's capital in 1931. Name the book and the real authors.

9. Who succeeded Milton Work as America's bridge expert? (Hint: he had two bestsellers in 1931.)

10. Vash Young wrote a 1932 bestseller on how to lick the depression blues. Name it.

† † †

70.   FOLLOW THE STAR

(Each question is a clue to this actress's identity.)

1.   She was born in Canada in 1869.

*   *   *

2.   In 1910 she appeared in *Tillie's Nightmare.*

*   *   *

3.   Mack Sennett talked her into making a film version of *Tillie's Nightmare,* called *Tillie's Punctured Romance.*

*   *   *

4.   By 1928 she was a flop and was thinking of taking a job as a housemaid.

*   *   *

5.   Her friend Frances Marion wrote a filmplay for her and sold it to Thalberg. The film was *The Callahans and the Murphys.*

*   *   *

6.   She played opposite Garbo in *Anna Christie.*

*   *   *

7.   She often appeared with Polly Moran.

*   *   *

8.   Wallace Beery starred with her in *Min and Bill.*

*   *   *

9. Beery also starred with her in *Tugboat Annie*.

*   *   *

10. She said, "You're only as good as your last picture."

Her name:

†   †   †

71. "ONE MAN'S FAMILY"

† † † † †

1. What was their last name?

        *   *   *

2. Where did they live?

        *   *   *

3. Name Henry's wife.

        *   *   *

4. Who was the oldest son?

        *   *   *

5. What did he do in World War I?

        *   *   *

6. Where did he live?

        *   *   *

7. Who was Teddy?

        *   *   *

8. Name Hazel's two husbands.

        *   *   *

9. Name Hazel's two sons by her first husband.

        *   *   *

10. Who was Claudia married to?

*   *   *

11. Who was Claudia's twin brother?

*   *   *

12. Whom did he marry?

*   *   *

13. Name Jack's wife.

*   *   *

14. How many children did they have?

†   †   †

72. VERSATILE KARLOFF

† † † † †

Match Boris Karloff's role and the movie:

1. He kills a stool pigeon in prison.
2. He is a revolutionary in the kingdom of El Dorania.
3. He's a crooked gambler who tries to cheat a small-town barber.
4. He is a fake clergyman.
5. He is a Svengali-like impresario.
6. He runs a fake mission.
7. He runs a narcotics ring.
8. He is a brutish butler.
9. He is a religious fanatic.
10. He is a Jew-hating baron.
11. He owns a nightclub.

  a) *The Miracle Man*
  b) *The Lost Patrol*
  c) *Behind the Mask*
  d) *The Criminal Code*
  e) *Smart Money*
  f) *Five Star Final*
  g) *The Old Dark House*
  h) *The House of Rothschild*
  i) *Night World*
  j) *Cracked Nuts*
  k) *The Mad Generation*

† † †

73. PLAY BALL!

† † † † †

Name the National League Most Valuable Players and their teams:

1932 _____

1933 _____

1934 _____

1935 _____

1936 _____

1937 _____

1938 _____

1939 _____

1940 _____

1941 _____

† † †

74. KNOCKOUT MOVIES

Match the prizefighting movie and the star:

1. *The Life of Jimmy Dolan*   a) Wayne Morris
2. *Winner Take All*   b) Joe E. Brown
3. *Hold Everything*   c) Marion Davies
4. *Dumbbells in Ermine*   d) John Payne
5. *City for Conquest*   e) Douglas
   Fairbanks, Jr.
6. *Kid Nightingale*   f) James Cagney
7. *The Kid Comes Back*   g) Pat O'Brien
8. *Kid Galahad*   h) Edward G.
   Robinson
9. *The Personality Kid*   i) Arthur Kennedy
10. *Cain and Mabel*   j) Robert Armstrong

75. WHEN EVERY STUDIO HAD AN ORGANIST

✝ ✝ ✝ ✝ ✝

Match the theme song with the radio show:

1. "The Guiding Light"		a)	"The Song of Bernadette"
2. "Against the Storm"		b)	"Rose of Tralee"
3. "Backstage Wife"		c)	"Valse Bluette"
4. "Big Sister"		d)	"Aphrodite"
5. "Hilltop House"		e)	Brahm's "Lullaby"
6. "When a Girl Marries"		f)	"How Can I Leave You?"
7. "Valiant Lady"		g)	"Clair de Lune"
8. "Today's Children"		h)	"Aphrodite"
9. "The Story of Mary Marlin"		i)	"Estrellita"
10. "Stella Dallas"		j)	"Drigo's Serenade"

✝ ✝ ✝

76.   IT'S ONLY A PAPER PICTURE

Match the newspaper movie and the star:

1. *The Pay-Off*   a) Joan Blondell
2. *Front Page Woman*   b) Edward G. Robinson
3. *Blessed Event*   c) Clark Gable
4. *Love Is a Racket*   d) James Cagney
5. *A Dispatch from Reuters* e) James Dunn
6. *Back in Circulation*   f) Dick Powell
7. *Marry the Girl*   g) Bette Davis
8. *Hi, Nellie!*   h) Douglas Fairbanks, Jr
9. *Picture Snatcher*   i) Mary Boland
10. *The Finger Points*   j) Paul Muni

77. PAST PLEASURES

1. Name the composer and the showman who appeared on commemorative half-dollars in 1936.

* * *

2. Who flew from Los Angeles to New York in less than eight hours in 1937?

* * *

3. What was "The Voice of Niagara"?

* * *

4. Who died in Ormond Beach, Fla. in 1937 at the age of 98?

* * *

5. Who kayoed Jim Braddock in eight rounds in 1937?

* * *

6. The Townsend plan was a) a national pension plan; b) a disarmament plan; c) a suburban community-development scheme; or d) an agreement between the recording industry and the musicians' union?

* * *

7. In 1934, which company began the large-scale raising and cultivation of soy beans: a) General Foods; b) Ford Motor Co.; c) the King Ranch; or d) Campbell Soup?

*   *   *

8. *The Barretts of Wimpole Street* starred a) Robert Donat and Elissa Landi; b) Norma Shearer and Fredric March; or c) Luise Rainer and William Powell?

*   *   *

9. "Smoke Gets in Your Eyes" was written by a) Duke Ellington; b) Hoagy Carmichael; c) George and Ira Gershwin; or d) Jerome Kern?

*   *   *

10. The 1945 Rose Bowl was won by a) Georgia Tech; b) Duke; c) Texas Christian; or d) Southern California?

† † †

78. CAPTAIN FROM HOLLYWOOD

Match the actors and the film:

1. Errol Flynn, M.D., becomes a pirate.
2. Robert Donat played Parnell.
3. "Mona Lisa" was the theme song of this Alan Ladd story.
4. Who cost John Payne his ship?
5. To Botany Bay with Brian Aherne, Victor McLaglen, Paul Lukas, and John Carradine.
6. Gregory Peck fights Bonaparte.
7. Shirley Temple in a lighthouse.
8. Spencer Tracy with a Portuguese accent.
9. Alec Guinness enjoys every mariner's dream.
10. Tyrone Power and Jean Peters, glitter and gold, and a resounding score.

    a) *Captains Courageous*
    b) *Captain China*
    c) *Captain from Castile*
    d) *Captain Carey, U.S.A.*
    e) *Captain Boycott*
    f) *Captain January*
    g) *The Captain's Paradise*
    h) *Captain Blood*
    i) *Captain Horatio Hornblower*
    j) *Captain Fury*

79. YOU KNOW ME, AL

† † † † †

Name the American League Most Valuable Players and their teams:

1932 _____
1933 _____
1934 _____
1935 _____
1936 _____
1937 _____
1938 _____
1939 _____
1940 _____
1941 _____

† † †

80. JUKEBOX IN THE LOBBY

† † † † †

Match the song and the movie:

1. "Aba Daba Honeymoon"		a)	*Gold Diggers of 1935*
2. "But Not for Me"		b)	*I Live for Love*
3. "You'll Never Know"		c)	*Stars over Broadway*
4. "How about You?"		d)	*Lady Be Good*
5. "Love is Where You Find It"		e)	*Two Weeks with Love*
6. "Sing, You Son of a Gun"		f)	*Hollywood Hotel*
7. "Carry Me Back to the Lone Prairie"		g)	*Babes on Broadway*
8. "Lullaby of Broadway"		h)	*Garden of the Moon*
9. "Broken Melody"		i)	*Girl Crazy*
10. "Mine Alone"		j)	*Fashions of 1934*

† † †

81. THE SPOKEN WORD

† † † † †

Match the radio entertainers and their catchphrases:

1. Hildegarde
2. Don McNeil
3. The Mad Russian
4. Charlie McCarthy
5. Fibber McGee
6. Jack Benny
7. Cass Daley
8. Joe Kelly
9. Cap'n Henry
10. Ralph Edwards

a) "How do you do-o-o?"
b) "Now cut that out!"
c) "It's only the beginnin', folks!"
d) "I said it and I'm glad!"
e) "Hello, hello, everybody, everywhere."
f) "I'll clip ya'. So help me, I'll mow you down!"
g) "Be good to yourself!"
h) "Dad-rat the rat-ratted . . ."
i) "Give me a little traveling music, Harry."
j) "Aren't we devils?"

† † †

82. ALL SINGING

† † † † †

Who sang

1. "Tiger Rag" in *The Big Broadcast:* a) Bing Crosby; b) Cab Calloway; c) The Boswell Sisters; or d) The Mills Brothers?

* * *

2. "By Myself" in *The Band Wagon:* a) Jack Buchanan; b) Oscar Levant; c) Cyd Charisse; or d) Fred Astaire?

* * *

3. "The Lady Is a Tramp" in *Babes in Arms:* a) June Preisser; b) Betty Jayne; or c) Judy Garland?

* * *

4. "The Girl That I Marry" in *Annie Get Your Gun:* a) Keenan Wynn; b) Louis Calhern; c) Howard Keel; or d) Edward Arnold?

* * *

5. "I'll Build a Stairway to Paradise" in *An American in Paris:* a) Georges Guetary; b) Oscar Levant; c) Nina Foch; or d) Leslie Caron?

* * *

6. "A Pretty Girl Is Like a Melody" in *Alexander's Ragtime Band:* a) Don Ameche; b) Dixie Dunbar; c) Ethel Merman; or d) Tyrone Power?

7. "I'm in the Mood for Love" in *Every Night at Eight:* a) Ted Fiorito; b) George Raft; c) Frances Langford; or d) Alice Faye?

*   *   *

8. "Putting on the Ritz" in *Blue Skies:* a) Olga San Juan; b) Billy De Wolfe; c) Fred Astaire; or d) Joan Caulfield?

*   *   *

9. "Rap Tap on Wood" in *Born to Dance:* a) Eleanor Powell; b) James Stewart; c) Virginia Bruce; or d) Buddy Ebsen?

*   *   *

10. "This Can't Be Love" in *"The Boys from Syracuse:* a) Joe Penner; b) Allan Jones; c) Charles Butterworth; d) Rosemary Lane; or e) Martha Raye?

*   *   *

11. "Everybody Sing" in *Broadway Melody of 1938:* a) George Murphy; b) Robert Taylor; c) Sophie Tucker; d) Judy Garland; or e) Eleanor Powell?

†   †   †

83.   BOOKMAKERS

† † † † †

1. Who wrote *Kiss Me, Deadly?*

*   *   *

2. Who wrote *The Exurbanites?*

*   *   *

3. Who wrote *I Led Three Lives?*

*   *   *

4. Who wrote *The Status Seekers?*

*   *   *

5. Who wrote *'Twixt Twelve and Twenty?*

*   *   *

6. Who wrote *Not as a Stranger?*

*   *   *

7. Who wrote *Berlin Diary?*

*   *   *

8. Who wrote *Native Son?*

*   *   *

9. Who wrote *Disputed Passage?*

*   *   *

10. Who wrote *The Yearling?*

11. Who wrote *Northwest Passage?*

*   *   *

12. Who wrote *The Rains Came?*

*   *   *

13. Who wrote *Drums along the Mohawk?*

*   *   *

14. Who wrote *The People, Yes?*

*   *   *

15. Who wrote *Inside Europe?*

*   *   *

16. Who wrote *The Daring Young Man on the Flying Trapeze?*

†   †   †

84. COMIC QUESTIONS

† † † † †

1. The Spectre was the ghost of whom?

* * *

2. What was Dr. Fate's real name?

* * *

3. Andre, Stanislaus, Hendrickson, Olaf, Chuck, and Chop Chop made up what group?

* * *

4. What was Airboy's real name?

* * *

5. "Cocky" Roach and the Judge were part of what group?

* * *

6. What was the Heap's real name?

* * *

7. What was Wonder Woman's real name?

† † †

85. THE BIG STEM

† † † † †

Match the clue with the movie:

1. Racketeer George Raft vs. Pat O'Brien.
2. Reporter Ralph Byrd goes to prison.
3. Dick Powell takes a trip.
4. Wini Shaw is sponsored by gambler Lyle Talbot.
5. Remember *Three on a Match?* Here's Ann Sheridan, Marie Wilson, and Margaret Lindsay doing the same bit.
6. Walter Winchell's broadcast solves a mystery.
7. "Hey, let's put on a show!" with Jed Prouty, Bessie Love, and Mary Doran.
8. "That's not a bad idea, let's put on a show too!" with Lena Horne, George Murphy, and Ginny Simms.
9. Victor McLaglen, ZaSu Pitts, and Patsy Kelly also take a trip.
10. Charlie Winninger can't believe that vaudeville is dead.

   a) *Broadway Limited*
   b) *Broadway*
   c) *The Broadway Melody*
   d) *Broadway Big Shot*
   e) *Give My Regards to Broadway*
   f) *Broadway thru a Keyhole*
   g) *Broadway Gondolier*
   h) *Broadway Rhythm*
   i) *Broadway Hostess*
   j) *Broadway Musketeers*

† † †

86. ANNUAL EVENTS

† † † † †

1. It all took place in what year: Damon Runyon Cancer Fund was founded, phone service was installed on railroad trains, and a C-45 Army plane crashed into the Bank of Manhattan building in New York.

* * *

2. It all took place in what year: Kathleen Winsor wrote *Forever Amber,* Katharine Hepburn and Walter Huston appeared in *Dragon Seed,* and Arlen and Mercer wrote "Ac-cent-tchu-ate the Positive."

* * *

3. It all took place in what year: Gregory Peck appeared in *The Keys of the Kingdom,* Gary Cooper and Ingrid Bergman starred in *Saratoga Trunk,* Betty MacDonald had a bestseller in *The Egg and I,* and Warren and Mercer wrote "On the Atchison, Topeka and the Santa Fe."

* * *

4. It all took place in what year: Paul Lukas and Bette Davis appeared in *Watch on the Rhine,* Mr. Julius Klorfein bought Jack Benny's violin for $1 million in war bonds, and William Saroyan's *The Human Comedy* was a bestseller.

† † †

87. BUSY STARS

† † † † †

1. Name one star who appeared in all these movies: *Random Harvest, Girl Crazy, Assignment in Brittany, Mrs. Miniver.*

* * *

2. Name one star who appeared in all these movies: *If Winter Comes, Words and Music, It's a Big Country, Houdini, Walking My Baby Back Home.*

* * *

3. Name one star who appeared in all these movies: *That Midnight Kiss, The Toast of New Orleans, The Great Caruso, Because You're Mine.*

* * *

4. Name one star who appeared in all these movies: *The Life and Death of Colonel Blimp, The Prisoner of Zenda, The End of the Affair.*

* * *

5. Name one star who appeared in all these movies: *Somewhere I'll Find You, A Guy Named Joe, Dr. Gillespie's Criminal Case, Two Girls and a Sailor.*

* * *

6. Name one star who appeared in all these movies: *The Postman Always Rings Twice, Marshal of Mesa City, Secrets of a Nurse, The Count of Monte Cristo, Parachute Jumper.*

* * *

7. Name one star who appeared in all these movies: *Beau Brummell, Don Juan, Jennie Gerhardt, Page Miss Glory, Dodsworth, Cynthia.*

* * *

8. Name one star who appeared in all these movies: *The Love Parade, The Vagabond King, Monte Carlo, Let's Go Native, The Lottery Bride.*

* * *

9. Name one star who appeared in all these movies: *Ebb Tide, Bringing Up Baby, Four Men and a Prayer, How Green Was My Valley.*

* * *

10. Name one star who appeared in all these movies: *We Were Dancing, Highway to Freedom, Hitler's Madman, Three Men in White, Whistle Stop, The Hucksters.*

† † †

127

88. REMOTE MEMORIES

† † † † †

Who broadcast from:

1. Town Hall, New York City

 *   *   *

2. Hotel Taft

 *   *   *

3. The Twentieth Century Limited

 *   *   *

4. Shrine Auditorium

 *   *   *

5. Shrine of the Little Flower

 *   *   *

6. New Amsterdam Roof

 *   *   *

7. Ryman Auditorium

 *   *   *

8. Capitol Theatre in Wheeling, W. Va.

† † †

89.   THE GREAT PROFILE

Name the John Barrymore film:

1. He plays a gentleman thief, based on a novel by E. W. Hornung, a role later taken over by House Peters, Ronald Colman, and David Niven.

* * *

2. He matches wits with a teacher of mathematics.

* * *

3. He is an English dandy.

* * *

4. He is Sergeant Ivan Markov, soldier in the army of the Czar (story by Erich von Stroheim).

* * *

5. He is Francois Villon, poet and thief.

* * *

6. He is Lord Strathpeffer, an aristocratic lush.

* * *

7. He hypnotizes a model into becoming a great singer.

* * *

8. He is a ballet master.

*   *   *

9. He steals the *Mona Lisa* from the Louvre.

*   *   *

10. He is Larry Renault, an ex-matinee idol.

†   †   †

90. K. O. RECALLS

† † † † †

Match the boxer with his nickname or nom de fists:

1. The Herkimer Hurricane
2. Mushy Callahgan
3. The Ambling Alp
4. The Orchid Man
5. Kid Chocolate
6. The Pittsburgh Kid
7. The Scotch Wop
8. Wild Bull of the Pampas
9. The Georgia Deacon
10. The Hawk

a) Elizio Sardinias
b) Tiger Flowers
c) Kid Gavilan
d) Lou Ambers
e) Billy Conn
f) Luis Angel Firpo
g) Vincent Morris Scheer
h) Primo Carnera
i) Georges Carpentier
j) Johnny Dundee

† † †

91. HIT PARADE OF THE AIR

† † † † †

Match the radio show and the theme song:

1. "Your Hit Parade"
2. "Kitty Keene"
3. "The Voice of Firestone"
4. "Life with Luigi"
5. "A Tale of Today"
6. "Moon River"
7. "Stoopnagle and Budd"
8. "One Man's Family"
9. "The Shadow"
10. "The O'Neills"

a) "Omphale's Spinning Wheel"
b) "Chopsticks"
c) "Your Lucky Day"
d) "None but the Lonely Heart"
e) "Londonderry Air"
f) "Oh, Marie"
g) "If I Could Tell You"
h) "Caprice Viennois"
i) "Destiny Waltz"
j) "Coronation March"

† † †

92. "A FAR, FAR BETTER THING . . ."

Ronald Colman movies:

1. He plays an idealistic M.D. searching for a cure to the plague.

*   *   *

2. He is Paul Goddard, a Russian nobleman/cab driver.

*   *   *

3. He is Sydney Carton.

*   *   *

4. He is Robert Conway.

*   *   *

5. He is Rudolf Rasendyll.

*   *   *

6. He is Francois Villon.

*   *   *

7. He is Dick Heldar.

*   *   *

8. He is Professor Michael Lightcap, who helps an accused arsonist.

*   *   *

9.   He is Charles Rainier, a wounded soldier with amnesia.

*   *   *

10.   He is a Boston Brahmin whose children are giving him trouble.

†   †   †

93. DUSTY NOVELS

1. Who wrote *The Shepherd of the Hills, The Calling of Dan Matthews,* and *The Winning of Barbara Worth?*

* * *

2. Who wrote *Saturday's Child, Rose of the World, Hildegarde, Barberry Bush,* and *Margaret Yorke?*

* * *

3. Who wrote *Girl of the Limberlost* and *Freckles Comes Home?*

* * *

4. Who wrote the *X Bar X Boys* books?

* * *

5. Who wrote the *Tom Swift* books?

† † †

94. FOR THE DURATION

1. What did Adolph A. Berle, Raymond Moley, Rexford Tugwell, and Felix Frankfurter have in common?

* * *

2. How much a week did you need, according to a 1941 song, to "keep filled with porkchops from the AP, with enough for food, rent, phone, clothes, picture shows, laundry, and the Morris Plan"?

* * *

3. What was the name of Norway's exiled king?

* * *

4. Prefabricated office buildings were called: a) Steelies; b) Roosevelt Huts; c) Duration Shacks; or d) Tempos?

* * *

5. What were L Orders and M Orders?

* * *

6. How did A, B, and C stickers differ?

* * *

7. What was the GOC?

* * *

8. What were the planes flown on Doolittle's raid on Japan?

*   *   *

9.   Who commanded the Marines in the Solomons?

*   *   *

10.   What force did Montgomery command at El Ala-mein?

†   †   †

95. CAMERA HISTORY

1. Thelma Todd, Betty Mack, and Muriel Evans were associated with a) Charlie Chase; b) Edgar Kennedy; or c) Buster Keaton?

*　　*　　*

2. Who was featured in all six of these marital movies: *Don't Tell the Wife, Next Time I Marry, You Can't Fool Your Wife, Easy to Wed, Her Husband's Affairs,* and *Guide for the Married Man?*

*　　*　　*

3. Who was featured in both of these "meety" movies: *Meet Nero Wolfe* and *Meet John Doe?*

*　　*　　*

4. Who was featured in these four "streety" movies: *Tobacco Road, The Forbidden Street, Where the Sidewalk Ends,* and *Madison Avenue?*

*　　*　　*

5. Who was the actor starring in all four of these movies: *China Passage, King of Chinatown, China Girl,* and *China Sky?*

*　　*　　*

6. Dennis Morgan in *Harmony Lane,* Don Ameche in *Swanee River,* and Bill Shirley in *I Dream of Jeanie* all played what role?

7. Who wrote and directed *The First of the Few:* a) Leslie Howard; b) John Ford; c) John Huston; or d) Errol Flynn?

* * *

8. Who wrote as well as acted in *Adventures of Captain Fabian:* a) Leslie Howard; b) John Huston; c) Errol Flynn; or d) Stewart Granger?

* * *

9. James Ellison in *The Plainsman,* Louis Calhern in *Annie Get Your Gun,* and Charlton Heston in *Pony Express* all played what character?

* * *

10. Name the character played by Dudley Field Malone in *Mission to Moscow* and Patrick Wymark in *Operation Crossbow.*

† † †

96. SEE YOU IN THE FUNNY PAPERS

† † † † †

Match the comics character with his real identity:

1. The Blue Beetle   a) Reed Richards
2. The Face   b) Ben Grimm
3. Madam Fatal   c) Dan Garrett
4. Plastic Man   d) Tony Trent
5. Mister Fantastic   e) Eel O'Brian
6. The Thing   f) Bill Perkins
7. Manhunter   g) Roy Lincoln
8. The Human Bomb   h) Dan Richards
9. The Human Torch   i) Johnny Storm
10. The Mouthpiece   j) Richard Stanton

† † †

97.   ALIAS THE CHAMP

Match the boxer with his nom de fists:

1. The Jewel of the Ghetto   a) Arnold Cream
2. The Human Windmill   b) Ruby Goldstein
3. Hard Rock from Down Under   c) Jake LaMotta
4. Nebraska Wildcat   d) Max Schmeling
5. Beau Jack   e) Sidney Walker
6. Sweetwater Swatter   f) Tom Heeney
7. The Bronx Bull   g) Ace Hudkins
8. The Toy Bulldog   h) Lew Jenkins
9. Jersey Joe   i) Harry Greb
10. The Black Uhlan   j) Mickey Walker

98. THERE'S A WAR ON, YOU KNOW

† † † † †

Match the wartime agency with its job:

1. OPA   a) coordinated government agencies
2. WPB   b) coordinated weapon research
3. WLB   c) settled labor-management problems
4. WMC   d) controlled prices and priorities of civilian supplies
5. WRA   e) coordinated wartime economy
6. OWI   f) ran Japanese internment camps
7. WSA   g) coordinated public relations
8. OWM   h) controlled the merchant marine
9. OSRD   i) coordinated manpower demands
10. ODT   j) made the trains run on time

† † †

99. DANGEROUS MOVIES

† † † † †

Match the movie with its stars:

1. *Dangerous Mission*	a) Esther Williams	I. Vincent Price
2. *Dangerous Partners*	b) Ella Raine	II. Fernando Lamas
3. *A Dangerous Profession*	c) Mary Boland	III. John Garfield
4. *Danger—Love at Work*	d) Piper Laurie	IV. James Craig
5. *Danger Signal*	e) Jeanne Crain	V. Michael Rennie
6. *Dangerous*	f) Gail Patrick	VI. Akim Tamiroff
7. *Dangerous to Know*	g) Faye Emerson	VII. Franchot Tone
8. *Dangerously They Live*	h) Signe Hasso	VIII. Zachary Scott
9. *Dangerous When Wet*	i) Nancy Coleman	IX. Ann Sothern
10. *Dangerous Crossing*	j) Bette Davis	X. George Raft

† † †

100.   GREAT THEMES

† † † † †

Match the theme song with the radio show:

1. "The Bob Burns Show"
2. "The Romance of Helen Trent"
3. "Pretty Kitty Kelly"
4. "The Eddie Cantor Show"
5. "The Road of Life"

6. "Orphans of Divorce"
7. "Joyce Jordan, Girl Interne"
8. "Escape"
9. "Gene Autry's Melody Ranch"
10. "Pepper Young's Family"

11. "Our Gal Sunday"

12. "The Hour of Charm"

a) "Poem"
b) "American Patrol March"
c) "Night on Bald Mountain"
d) "Back in the Saddle Again"
e) "I'll Take You Home Again, Kathleen"
f) "Juanita"
g) "Red River Valley"
h) "Au Matin"
i) "Kerry Dance"
j) First Movement, "Pathetique Symphony"
k) "The Arkansas Traveler"
l) "One Hour with You"

† † †

101. A STARRY BOOKSHELF

† † † † †

Match the autobiography with its author:

1. *His Eye Is on the Sparrow*
2. *I'll Cry Tomorrow*
3. *Memoirs of a Professional Cad*
4. *Little World, Hello*
5. *Faith Is a Song*
6. *Who Could Ask for Anything More*
7. *Sing as We Go*
8. *Thursday's Child*
9. *Present Indicative*
10. *Such Sweet Compulsion*

a) Noel Coward
b) Gracie Fields
c) Ethel Merman
d) Jessica Dragonette
e) Geraldine Farrar
f) Eartha Kitt
g) George Sanders
h) Lillian Roth
i) Jimmy Savo
j) Ethel Waters

† † †

102. QUIET, WE'RE ON THE AIR!

1. Who led "The Band of a Thousand Melodies"?

* * *

2. Who led The Studebaker Champions?

* * *

3. Did Chester Morris ever play Boston Blackie on radio?

* * *

4. Who were Baba, Ghangi, Little Fox, and Koola?

* * *

5. Who played the Happy Postman on "The Burns and Allen Show"?

* * *

6. Jason Robards, Sr. played what adventure-series hero?

* * *

7. How many Charlie Chans can you recall?

* * *

8. Name the stooges of a) Judy Canova; b) Phil Harris; c) Phil Baker; and d) Eddie Cantor.

146

9. Who presided over: a) "The Old Fashioned Revival Hour"; b) "National Radio Pulpit"; c) "National Vespers"; and d) "The Lutheran Hour"?

* * *

10. With whom did Rex Marshall share the hosting chores on "A Date with Rex"?

† † †

103.　DARK MOVIES

1.　Olivia De Havilland worked twice as hard in this twin-sister movie.

*　　*　　*

2.　Psychology plays an important role in this Bill Holden–Lee J. Cobb flicker.

*　　*　　*

3.　Edward G. Robinson has a gambling itch; Genevieve Tobin suffers.

*　　*　　*

4.　Warren William and Bette Davis help candidate Guy Kibbee.

*　　*　　*

5.　Claire Trevor and John Wayne in a Quantrill raider story.

*　　*　　*

6.　Mark Stevens is helped out of a murder charge by —Lucille Ball!

*　　*　　*

7.　Fredric March and Herbert Marshall vie for Merle Oberon.

* * *

8. Gangsters hunt for Charlton Heston.

* * *

9. Bogie hides out in Bacall's apartment.

* * *

10. Bette Davis dies beautifully.

† † †

104.   THEY PAID THE BILLS

Match the sponsor and the radio show:

1. Household Finance Corporation
2. Wildroot Cream-Oil
3. Bugler Tobacco
4. Helbros Watches

5. Tums
6. Texaco
7. Revere Camera
8. Bristol-Myers
9. Sanka Coffee
10. Oxydol

a) "Baby Snooks Show"
b) "Quick as a Flash"
c) "The Beulah Show"
d) "Metropolitan Opera Broadcasts"
e) "Name the Movie"
f) "Ma Perkins"
g) "Welcome Valley"
h) "Plantation Party"
i) "Sam Spade"
j) "Mr. District Attorney"

105. YEAR: 1946

1. The Signal Corps sent a radar beam where?

* * *

2. What world-famous organization disbanded?

* * *

3. *The Foxes of Harrow, The Miracle of the Bells,* and *The Snake Pit* were published. Who were the authors?

* * *

4. Where were the A-bomb tests carried out?

* * *

5. What country received its independence on July 4?

* * *

6. Who was absolved of responsibility for Pearl Harbor by a Congressional committee?

* * *

7. Who was asked for his resignation by Harry S. Truman?

* * *

8. Who gave the UN its New York home?

* * *

9. Who was the first American citizen to be canonized a saint?

* * *

10. Name the National League teams that played 19 innings.

106. COME AND GO

† † † † †

1. Edward Arnold had the big part, but Walter Brennan won a Best Supporting Actor Oscar in this Edna Ferber story.

* * *

2. James Cagney, James Gleason, and Gig Young raise their glasses.

* * *

3. Shirley Booth won an Oscar in this film version of a William Inge play.

* * *

4. Jolson sings; Keeler dances.

* * *

5. Van Johnson heads a Nisei outfit.

* * *

6. The Marx Brothers take a train ride.

* * *

7. Bing and Barry as men of the cloth.

* * *

8. Mae West has nothing better to do than seduce Randolph Scott.

*   *   *

9. Loretta Young and Celeste Holm as French nuns.

*   *   *

10. Jimmy Stewart marries Hedy Lamarr to help her.

†   †   †

107. JUST THE OTHER DAY

† † † † †

1. Who was the contestant on "Twenty-One" who knew the names of the only three ballplayers to make more than 3,500 hits and the name of the character who sings "Sempre Libre" in *La Traviata?*

* * *

2. Who played Davy Crockett?

* * *

3. What was Ruth Simmons famous for?

* * *

4. What were poodles, ducktails, and Apaches?

* * *

5. Who sang "Till I Waltz Again with You"?

* * *

6. Who sang "You, You, You"?

* * *

7. Who sang "Why Don't You Believe Me"?

* * *

8. Who sang "Little Things Mean a Lot"?

* * *

9. Who sang "Here in My Heart"?

* * *

10. Who sang "Kiss of Fire"?

† † †

108. COMICS, WHITE TIE AND TAILS

Ibis was "The Invincible," but do you remember how these other comic-book magicians were described?

1. Yarko
2. Jupiter
3. Stardust
4. Magar
5. Kardak
6. Red Reeves
7. Mystico
8. Monako
9. Nardir
10. Merzak
11. Balbo
12. Marvelo

a) The Boy Magician
b) Master Magician
c) The Mystic Magician
d) The Mystic
e) Monarch of Magicians
f) Prince of Magic
g) The Wonder Man
h) Master of Magic
i) Boy Magician
j) The Super Wizard
k) The Great Master Magician

109.   GINGER WITHOUT FRED

† † † † †

Match the Ginger Rogers pictures with her co-stars:

1. *Professional Sweetheart*

2. *Sitting Pretty*

3. *Finishing School*

4. *20 Million Sweethearts*

5. *Romance in Manhattan*

6. *Star of Midnight*

7. *In Person*

8. *Stage Door*

9. *Having Wonderful Time*

10. *Bachelor Mother*

11. *Fifth Avenue Girl*

12. *Kitty Foyle*

a) Walter Connolly, Tim Holt, Louis Calhern

b) Dennis Morgan, Gladys Cooper

c) Gregory Ratoff, Franklin Pangborn

d) David Niven, Charles Coburn

e) Douglas Fairbanks, Jr., Red Skelton

f) Adolphe Menjou, Jack Carson

g) George Brent, Alan Mowbray

h) William Powell, Paul Kelly

i) Francis Lederer, J. Farrell MacDonald

j) Dick Powell, Allan Jenkins

k) Bruce Cabot, John Halliday

l) Jack Oakie, Jack Haley

† † †

110. COFFIN-NAIL TRIVIA

† † † † †

1. Complete these ads: a) "_____ Use Only the Center Leaves—The Center Leaves Give You the Mildest Smoke." b) "_____ —They Never Get On Your Nerves." c) "The Largest Selling Cigaret at Sherman Billingsley's Stork Club—_____" d) "Apple Honey helps guard _____ from cigarette dryness"

* * *

2. Whose radio music shows were sponsored by: a) Camels; b) Chesterfields; c) Raleighs and Kools; d) Old Golds?

* * *

3. Who made these songs famous: a) "Smoke! Smoke! Smoke! That Cigarette"; b) "Reefer Man"; c) "Two Cigarettes in the Dark"; d) "Smoke Dreams"; e) "Cigarettes, Whiskey and Wild Wild Women"; f) "Smoke Rings"; and g) "Love Is Like a Cigarette"?

* * *

4. Who was "the pride of New Orleans"?

* * *

5. Which cigarette "pleases as it eases"?

* * *

6. What did White Rolls, Paul Jones, and Twenty Grand have in common?

*　　*　　*

7. Complete this commercial: "Yes, Betty Petty is keeping the wires hot. But there's nothing phony about the new impartial tests of five leading brands of cigarettes that now prove _____ a truly better smoke."

†　　†　　†

111. MATINEE QUOTABLES

† † † † †

Match the quote and the movie:

1. "Because he drank, you're a lush. Because he loved women, you're a tramp."
2. "I play the stock market of the spirit and I sell short."
3. "This is the worst torture ever invented; put us in a bug-infested cell and fix it so we can't scratch."
4. "There are times in the presence of your Majesty when I feel myself an amateur."
5. "They're refugees. They wouldn't pay their taxes."
6. "When the strong have devoured one another, the Christian ethic will again take over, the meek shall inherit the earth."
7. "In moments of calm, I'm quite drawn to you, Susan, but there have been no moments of calm."
8. "Good day, Mr. Dillard, I'm sorry to have troubled you."
9. "She didn't see me at all, but I'll bet a month hasn't gone by since, that I haven't thought of that girl."
10. "On your left you see the Iron Maiden of Nuremberg, sometimes known as the German statue of liberty."
11. "No man died more bravely, nor brought more honor to his regiment."

a) *The Lives of a Bengal Lancer*
b) *Jezebel*
c) *Citizen Kane*
d) *Bringing Up Baby*
e) *The Bad and the Beautiful*

f) *Above Suspicion*
g) *Lost Horizon*
h) *Fort Apache*
i) *The Fountainhead*
j) *The General Died at Dawn*
k) *The Prisoner of Zenda*

112.   HAVE A BALL

1.   Baseball's triple crown (highest batting average, most runs batted in, and most home runs) was won by a) Babe Ruth; b) Stan Musial; or c) Joe Dimaggio?

* * *

2.   Who was the first player to hit two grand-slam homers in one game?

* * *

3.   What were Al Smith, Jim Bagby, Jr., and Ken Keltner famous (or infamous) for?

* * *

4.   What was Carl Hubbell's astonishing feat in the 1934 All Star game?

* * *

5.   Who pitched the only no-hitter on an opening day?

* * *

6.   Who pitched the only two consecutive no-hitters?

* * *

7.   In what game did Babe Ruth call his homer?

* * *

8.   Who managed the Pittsburgh Pirates to their 1925 Series triumph?

9. Who managed the Cincinnati Reds to their Series win in 1940?

*　　*　　*

10. Who was the youngest player ever to play in a major league game?

†　　†　　†

113. FRANKIE'S FILMS

† † † † †

Match the Frank Sinatra song with the film in which he sang it:

1. "I'll Never Smile Again"
2. "Night and Day"
3. "I Couldn't Sleep a Wink Last Night"
4. "As Long as There's Music"
5. "The Charm of You"
6. "Ol' Man River"
7. "I Believe"
8. "Kisses and Tears"
9. "That Old Black Magic"
10. "One for My Baby"

a) *Double Dynamite*
b) *Till the Clouds Roll By*
c) *Las Vegas Nights*
d) *Reveille With Beverly*
e) *Meet Danny Wilson*
f) *It Happened in Brooklyn*
g) *Higher and Higher*
h) *Step Lively*
i) *Anchors Aweigh*
j) *Young at Heart*

† † †

114. PAST GLORIES

1. Who died in 1947, leaving a $600 million estate?

* * *

2. The one-billionth record pressed by RCA (1946) was a) "The Old Lamp Lighter"; b) "The Minute Waltz"; or c) "The Stars and Stripes Forever"?

* * *

3. Phone service was finally installed in 1946 on a) trains; b) planes; or c) Mississippi riverboats?

* * *

4. In 1944 the first five-star generals and admirals were appointed. Name them.

* * *

5. In 1943, Soviet agents killed what newspaper editor in New York?

* * *

6. Name the foreign statesman who was temporarily buried at Arlington National Cemetery in 1941.

* * *

7. What country asked for an armistice on June 17, 1940?

* * *

8. The Hatch Act a) prohibited poultry men from raising a certain number of chickens; b) subsidized the training of bombardiers; or c) prohibited civil servants from participating in politics?

* * *

9. In 1938, Felix Schlag was awarded $1,000 for a) designing the Jefferson-head nickel; b) coming in first in the Boston Marathon; or c) designing the trylon and perisphere for the New York World's Fair?

* * *

10. Who struck out 18 Detroit Tigers in a 1938 game?

† † †

115. CUTE KIDS

† † † † †

Match the child actor with the film:

1. *Lassie Come Home*   a) Peggy Ann Garner
2. *Our Vines Have*   b) Mitzi Green
   Tender Grapes
3. *Primrose Path*   c) Freddie
                          Bartholomew
4. *David Copperfield*   d) Roddy McDowell
5. *Curse of the Cat People*   e) Bobby Driscoll
6. *Skippy*   f) Jackie Cooper
7. *Once Upon a Time*   g) Ted Donaldson
8. *Song of the South*   h) Butch Jenkins
9. *A Tree Grows*   i) Ann Carter
   in Brooklyn
10. *Little Orphan Annie*   j) Joan Carroll

† † †

116. TV EMCEES

† † † † †

Who hosted:

1. "Hollywood Screen Test"

    * * *

2. "Star of the Family"

    * * *

3. "Fashion Magic"

    * * *

4. "On Your Way"

    * * *

5. "Floor Show"

† † †

117. LONG WAVES LONG AGO

1. Phillips H. Lord starred in what show?

* * *

2. What did Doc Hackett ("County Seat") and Dr. Benjamin Ordway ("Crime Doctor") have in common?

* * *

3. What was the other name of "The Vaseline Program"?

* * *

4. Who played "Hilda Hope, M.D."?

* * *

5. Name the girl interne who went on to practice medicine in Preston.

* * *

6. What show had Dr. Chandler married to Dr. Chandler?

* * *

7. What was Dr. Philip Carey's physical problem in "Of Human Bondage"?

* * *

8. Dr. Jim Brent was always asked to call surgery on what program?

*   *   *

9.   What did Drs. Karnac and Weird have in common?

*   *   *

10.   What did Drs. Lilienthal, Lanson, Abendrofth, Gordon, Scott, and Ellerbe have in common?

† † †

118. PICTURE THIS

1. What actor starred in these three heavenly movies: *An Angel from Texas, The Roots of Heaven,* and *Miracle of the White Stallions?*

* * *

2. Jean Arthur in *The Plainsman,* Frances Farmer in *Badlands of Dakota,* Jane Russell in *The Paleface,* and Judi Meredith in *The Raiders* all played what character?

* * *

3. Carlyle Blackwell, Jack Buchanan, Ronald Colman, Kenneth MacKenna, Ralph Richardson, Ray Milland, Tom Conway, John Lodge, and Walter Pidgeon all had turns playing what character?

* * *

4. Name the movie actor who starred in each of these TV shows: a) "The Thin Man"; b) "Heaven for Betsy"; c) "Mr. Adams and Eve"; d) "Peck's Bad Girl"; and e) "Leave It to Larry."

* * *

5. Joe E. Brown starred in the football comedy *Maybe It's Love;* who starred in *College Coach?*

* * *

6. Billie Dove starred in the smuggling drama *The Lady Who Dared;* who starred in *On the Border?*

170

7. Loretta Young starred in the department-store movie *Employees' Entrance;* who starred in the department-store movie *Play Girl?*

8. Douglas Fairbanks, Jr. starred in the railroad drama *Union Depot;* who starred in the railroad drama *I Am a Thief?*

9. Richard Barthelmess starred in the gambling drama *Midnight Alibi;* name the star of *Gambling Lady.*

10. Ann Sheridan starred in the racing movie *Little Miss Thoroughbred;* who starred in *Wine, Women and Horses?*

119.   YEAR: 1947

1. Which Senator-elect, opposed by Republicans, never took his seat?

* * *

2. One hundred documents took a railroad trip— why?

* * *

3. What was the blue flag with a white polar map, embraced by olive branches?

* * *

4. What came to a halt in Manhattan?

* * *

5. What were seen all over the country and never identified?

* * *

6. Who died in the KLM aircrash at Copenhagen?

* * *

7. Centralia and Texas City shared what grim honors?

* * *

8. Who wrote a) *Across the Wide Missouri;* b) *Gentleman's Agreement;* c) *Kingsblood Royal;* d) *Lydia Bailey;* e) *Marry for Money;* f) *Tales of the South Pacific;* and g) *Yankee Pasha?*

172

* * *

9. Who was sued for plagiarism, successfully?

* * *

10. Who made her debut with the Detroit Symphony Orchestra?

† † †

120. FOUR OF A KIND

† † † † †

1. John Garfield got his break in this picture. With Rosemary, Lola, and Priscilla Lane.
2. Zoltan Korda directed this tale of nastiness and cowardice vindicated.
3. DeMille directed Claudette Colbert, Herbert Marshall, and Mary Boland.
4. Phil Silvers blinked his way through this patriotic opus.
5. John Ford directed Richard Greene, George Sanders, David Niven, J. Edward Bromberg, and Loretta Young.
6. Here come those Lane girls again, helping Eddie Albert, a bankrupt.
7. Rex Harrison and Lilli Palmer living their way through marriage.
8. Erroll Flynn and Olivia De Havilland starred in this Michael Curtiz comedy.
9. Why, here are those Lane sisters again, married but unhappy.
10. Viveca Lindfors and Ralph Meeker stare at the Danube a lot.

a) *Four Wives*
b) *Four Jills in a Jeep*
c) *Four Feathers*
d) *Four Men and a Prayer*
e) *Four's a Crowd*
f) *The Four Poster*
g) *Four Daughters*
h) *Four Frightened People*
i) *Four Mothers*
j) *Four in a Jeep*

† † †

174

121.   TV OR NOT TV

1.   Kuda Bux and Dunninger both had ESP shows in the fifties. A third host, whose other specialities included art and acting, also had a show. Name him and his show.

*   *   *

2.   One of radio's great voices made a comeback on TV on "Handyman." Who was it?

*   *   *

3.   What did all these people have in common: Dave Garroway, Betsy Palmer, Frank Blair, Charles Van Doren, Jack Lescouli?

*   *   *

4.   Name at least three stars of the "Garroway at Large" show.

*   *   *

5.   Who co-hosted "The Morning Show" with Charlemane, the Lion?

*   *   *

6.   Name three regular singers on Steve Allen's "Tonight" show.

*   *   *

7.   Jack Parr hosted what quiz show?

8. Aside from the "Tonight" show, name three other TV shows hosted by Johnny Carson.

*   *   *

9. What was Perry Como's first TV show?

*   *   *

10. Who hosted "Sing It Again"?

†   †   †

122. LADIES & GENTS

† † † † †

Match the film with the stars and description:

1. Man escapes prison to redeem honor of his daughter. With Brian Donlevy, Miriam Hopkins, Preson Foster.
2. Conmen become involved with the finer things in life. With Cesar Romero and Milton Berle.
3. The life of a boxer. With Errol Flynn and Alexis Smith.
4. Writer poses as Jew to uncover anti-Semitism. With Gregory Peck and Celeste Holm.
5. Two girls make good in Paris. With Jane Russell and Marilyn Monroe.
6. Husband-hunting Hungarian girls take a Budapest apartment. With Janet Gaynor, Loretta Young, Constance Bennett.
7. Housekeeper tries to protect a family. With Ida Lupino and Louis Hayward.
8. Young couple are framed. With Sylvia Sidney and Gene Raymond.
9. A wealthy eccentric woman gets involved with criminals. With Fay Bainter and Ida Lupino.
10. An apple vendor is transmuted. With May Robson and Warren William.

a) *Ladies of the Big House* f) *Gentlemen Prefer Blondes*
b) *Ladies in Love* g) *Gentleman Jim*
c) *Gentleman's Agreement* h) *A Gentleman at Heart*
d) *Lady and the Mob* i) *A Gentleman after Dark*
e) *Ladies in Retirement* j) *Lady for a Day*

† † †

177

123.   THEY'RE HUMMING OUR THEME

† † † † †

Match the theme song and the radio show:

1. "The A & P Gypsies"
2. "Young Widder Brown"
3. "First Nighter"
4. "The Goldbergs"
5. "I Love a Mystery"
6. "Front Page Farrell"
7. "Aunt Jenny"
8. "Bachelor's Children"
9. "Shell Chateau"
10. "Mr. & Mrs. North"

a) "The Way You Look Tonight"
b) "In the Gloaming"
c) "About a Quarter to Nine"
d) "Valse Triste"
e) "Two Guitars"
f) "Ah! Sweet Mystery of Life"
g) "Believe Me, If All Those Endearing Young Charms"
h) "You and I Know"
i) "Neapolitan Nights"
j) "Serenade"

† † †

124.　YEAR: 1948

1.　Complete the song titles: a) "A, You're _____"; b) "Buttons and _____"; c) "Cuanto le _____"; d) "It's _____."

*　*　*

2.　The Pumpkin Papers were discovered in what Maryland community?

*　*　*

3.　Where was the world's largest telescope located?

*　*　*

4.　What was the 4,900-acre project that was opened this year?

*　*　*

5.　What did Petrillo head?

*　*　*

6.　Name the authors of a) *Crusade in Europe;* b) *How to Stop Worrying and Start Living;* c) *The Seven Story Mountain;* d) *The Big Fisherman;* e) *The Naked and the Dead;* f) *Raintree Country;* g) *Shannon's Way;* and h) *The Young Lions.*

*　*　*

7.　What movies starred a) Jane Wyman and Lew Ayers; b) Moira Shearer and Anton Walbrook; and c) John Wayne and Montgomery Clift?

*   *   *

8. Who presided at the Communist conspiracy trial in New York?

*   *   *

9. What government act admitted over 200,000 refugees?

*   *   *

10. "Judy Splinters" beat "The Masked Spooner" for a TV Emmy. Describe these two shows.

†   †   †

125.   BRIGHT IDEAS

† † † † †

Match the inventor and the invention:

1. Lydle D. Goodhue   a) Nylon

2. William Green   b) Electric shaver

3. Vannever Bush   c) Aerosol spray bomb

4. J. Presper Eckert and   d) Electronic
   John W. Mauchly   computer

5. Jacob Schick   e) Jet engine

6. Vladimir K. Zworykin   f) Polarizing glass

7. Frank Whittle   g) Automatic airplane
          pilot

8. Peter C. Goldmark   h) Radar

9. Wallace H. Carothers   i) Parking meter

10. Carlton C. Magee   j) Long-playing record

11. Edwin H. Land   k) Electron microscope

12. Robert A. Watson-Watt   l) Differential analyzer
                  computer

† † †

181

126. SING YOUR HEARTS OUT

† † † † †

1. "I'm True to the Navy" was sung in *Paramount on Parade* by a) Lillian Roth; b) Clara Bow; c) Mitzi Green; or d) Mary Brian?

* * *

2. "The Touch of Your Hand" in *Roberta* was sung by a) Irene Dunne; b) Lucille Ball; c) Ginger Rogers; or d) Claire Dodd?

* * *

3. "Why Am I Blue?" was sung in *Show Business* by a) Nancy Kelly; b) Joan Davis; c) George Murphy; or d) Constance Moore?

* * *

4. "The Music Goes Round and Round" was sung in *Sing, Baby, Sing* by a) Tony Martin; b) Dixie Dunbar; c) The Ritz Brothers; or d) Adolph Menjou?

* * *

5. "Eadie was a Lady" was sung in *Take a Chance* by a) June Knight; b) Dorothy Lee; or c) Lillian Roth?

* * *

6. "I've Got a Pocketful of Sunshine" was sung in *Thanks a Million* by a) The Yacht Club Boys; b) Patsy Kelly; c) Dick Powell; or d) Fred Allen?

7. "It Had to Be You" was sung in *I'll See You in My Dreams* by a) Frank Lovejoy; b) Danny Thomas; c) Jim Backus; or d) Doris Day?

*   *   *

8. "The Saga of Jenny" was sung in *Lady in the Dark* by a) Warner Baxter; b) Barry Sullivan; c) Ginger Rogers; or d) Mischa Auer?

*   *   *

9. "I Wanna Be in Winchell's Column" was sung in *Love and Hisses* by a) Simone Simon; b) Joan Davis; c) Bert Lahr; or d) Ruth Terry?

*   *   *

10. "Just One of Those Things" was sung in *Night and Day* by a) Mary Martin; b) Alexis Smith; c) Cary Grant; or d) Ginny Simms?

†   †   †

127. I WAS A TV ADDICT

1. Who hosted "Meet Your Cover Girl" and "Vanity Fair"?

* * *

2. Who starred in the TV production of *Marty?*

* * *

3. Who hosted "Beat the Clock"?

* * *

4. Who hosted "This Is Show Business"?

* * *

5. Who hosted "Two for the Money"?

* * *

6. Who was Joan in "I Married Joan"?

* * *

7. Who was Margie in "My Little Margie"?

* * *

8. Who was Irma in "My Friend Irma"? Who was her girlfriend?

* * *

9. Richard Denning and Barbara Britton starred in what show?

* * *

10. Who sang "The Ho-Ho Song"?

† † †

128. GOOD SPORTS

1. Was Benny Leonard known as a) The Ghetto Wizard or as b) Battling Levinsky?

* * *

2. Who won the U.S. and British Amateurs in 1934 and 1935?

* * *

3. On what team did Nat Holman, Johnny Beckman, Joe Lapchick, Chris Leonard, and Dutch Dehnert play?

* * *

4. What is Fred Perry famous for?

* * *

5. What is Roy Riegels famous for?

* * *

6. What was the 1940 NFL championship game famous for?

* * *

7. The Four Horsemen played for Notre Dame. For whom did the Seven Mules play? What were their names?

*   *   *

8. Brooklyn temporarily left Ebbets Field in 1956 and 1957. Where did they play 7 "home" games in each season?

*   *   *

9. To whom did Max Schmeling lose his title on a decision?

†   †   †

129. THEY MADE THE MOVIE

Match the memorable performer with the film:

1. A punch-drunk prizefighter in *Adventures of a Young Man*
2. Prince John in *The Adventures of Robin Hood*
3. A banker in *Johnny Guitar*
4. A hotel switchboard operator in *I Wake up Screaming*
5. A hotel clerk in *High Sierra*
6. A stool pigeon in *The Enforcer*
7. A prairie evangelist in *Duel in the Sun*
8. A priest in *Cry, the Beloved Country*
9. An eccentric medium in *Blithe Spirit*
10. The prosecuting attorney in *Anatomy of a Murder*
11. Pawnee Bill in *Annie Get Your Gun*
12. A criminal mastermind in *The Asphalt Jungle*

   a) Cornel Wilde
   b) Paul Newman
   c) Claude Rains
   d) George C. Scott
   e) Edward Arnold
   f) Sam Jaffe
   g) Margaret Rutherford
   h) Sidney Poitier
   i) Walter Huston
   j) Zero Mostel
   k) Mercedes McCambridge
   l) Elisha Cook, Jr.

130. VIDEO RIDDLES

1. Marilyn Monroe made her TV debut on whose show?

*   *   *

2. What TV show did Tallulah Bankhead moderate?

*   *   *

3. Eddie Albert hosted what variety show?

*   *   *

4. Pinkie Lee was one half of "Those Two." Who played the other half?

*   *   *

5. What was the name of Olsen and Johnson's TV show?

*   *   *

6. Who were the stars of the "Henny and Rocky Show"?

*   *   *

7. Who hosted "Do You Trust Your Wife"?

*   *   *

8. Who appeared as George Gobel's wife?

*   *   *

9. Who introduced "This Was the Week That Was"?

*   *   *

10. Who hosted "Blind Date," "Soldier Parade," and "Home"?

†   †   †

131. THE SILVER SCREEN

† † † † †

1. Name the character played by both David Wayne and Peter Lorre.

* * *

2. John Wayne, Thomas Mitchell, and Barry Fitzgerald appeared in a classic motion picture based on four one-act plays. Name the playwright, the film, and the director.

* * *

3. Name one actor featured in these three "audible" movies: *The Story of Alexander Graham Bell*, *Something to Shout About*, and *Rings Around the World*.

* * *

4. Name the eminent screenwriter behind *Journey into Fear*, *Background to Danger*, *The Mask of Dimitrios*, *The Way Ahead*, *Topkapi*, *The Cruel Sea*, *A Night to Remember*, and *The Wreck of the Mary Deare*.

* * *

5. Name one actress featured in all these "numerical" movies: *Thousands Cheer*, *Two Girls and A Sailor*, *Music for Millions*, *Two Sisters from Boston*, and *The Three Musketeers*.

* * *

6. Name one actor featured in these three "location" movies: *Adventure in Baltimore*, *Sands of Iwo Jima*, and *Johnny Reno*.

7. What do all these women have in common: Lillian Gish, Ida Lupino, Dorothy Arzner, Lilian Ducey, Julia Crawford Ivers, Lois Weber?

*   *   *

8. What was Loretta Young's ailment in *And Now Tomorrow?*

*   *   *

9. What was Phyllis Thaxter's ailment in *Bewitched?*

*   *   *

10. What was Loretta Young's ailment in *The Right of Way;* Frank Fay's ailment in *The Matrimonial Bed?*

†   †   †

132.   RADIO QUOTES

1. Who were "America's favorite young couple"?

*   *   *

2. What story of love and marriage was "laid in a world few Americans know"?

*   *   *

3. What program offered "for your enjoyment, supremely lovely songs and melodies that capture all hearts?"

*   *   *

4. Where did you "hear a dramatic mystery of suspense and intrigue"?

*   *   *

5. Who was the "glamorous, incredible hostess" of "The Big Show"?

*   *   *

6. "The clock in Glens Hall Falls Town Hall" told us it was time for what show?

*   *   *

7. What show told us that "somehow we keep hoping, don't we, that our dreams come true"?

8. What show featured "strange and fantastic stories, some legend, some hearsay, but all so interesting we'd like to pass them along to you"?

* * *

9. Who was "that wise man with the friendly smile and the cash for your correct answers"?

* * *

10. "Bullock's in downtown Los Angeles—one of America's great stores" proudly originated what "radio program for the nation"?

† † †

133.   AT THE STATE THEATRE

† † † † †

Match the movies and the stars:

1. *Wyoming*

2. *Virginia*

3. *Texas*

4. *Oklahoma!*

5. *New Mexico*

6. *Nevada*

7. *Montana*

8. *Mississippi*

9. *Maryland*

10. *Kentucky*

11. *California*

12. *Arizona*

a) William Holden and Claire Trevor

b) Jean Arthur and William Holden

c) Walter Brennan and Fay Bainter

d) Wallace Beery and Ann Rutherford

e) Barbara Stanwyck and Ray Milland

f) Loretta Young and Richard Greene

g) Madeleine Carroll and Fred MacMurray

h) Robert Mitchum and Anne Jeffreys

i) Lew Ayres and Marilyn Maxwell

j) Gordon MacRae and Shirley Jones

k) Errol Flynn and Alexis Smith

l) Bing Crosby and Joan Bennett

† † †

134. HARRY'S TEAM

† † † † †

Who filled these cabinet posts in Truman's second administration?

1. Vice President
2. Secretary of State
3. Secretary of the Treasury
4. Secretary of Defense
5. Attorney General
6. Postmaster General
7. Secretary of the Interior
8. Secretary of Agriculture
9. Secretary of Commerce
10. Secretary of Labor

a) Maurice J. Tobin
b) J. Howard McGrath
c) John W. Snyder
d) Charles F. Brannan
e) Alben W. Barkley
f) Charles Sawyer
g) George C. Marshall
h) Oscar L. Chapman
i) Dean G. Acheson
j) Jesse M. Donaldson

† † †

135. CINEMA COMMONERS

1. What do Deborah Kerr, Bette Davis, and Joan Fontaine have in common?

* * *

2. What do Cesar Romero, Walter Huston, Victor Mature, and Kirk Douglas have in common?

* * *

3. What do Orson Welles and Jose Ferrer have in common?

* * *

4. What do Tyrone Power, Lawrence Tierney, Macdonald Carey, and Audie Murphy have in common?

* * *

5. What do Ethel Grandin, Louise Vale, Mabel Ballin, and Virginia Bruce have in common with each other and with the actresses in Question 1?

* * *

6. What do Irving Cummings, Alan Hale, Norman Trevor, Colin Clive, and Orson Welles have in common?

* * *

7. What do Geraldine Ferrar, Angela Salloker, Ingrid Bergman, and Jean Seberg have in common?

*　*　*

8. What do Claude Raines, Warren William, and Louis Calhern have in common?

*　*　*

9. What do Tom Keene, George Duryea, and Richard Powers have in common?

†　†　†

136.   TV GHOSTS

1. Name the hosts of a) "Winky-Dink and You"; b) "Mr. I. Magination"; c) "Masquerade Party."

* * *

2. Who moderated "Down You Go"?

* * *

3. Who moderated "To Tell the Truth"?

* * *

4. Who moderated "Merry Mailman"?

* * *

5. "Who moderated "The Mickey Mouse Club"?

* * *

6. Robert Horton and Ward Bond played in what series?

* * *

7. Who starred in "Cheyenne"?

* * *

8. Who was "Wyatt Earp"?

* * *

9. Who hosted a) "The $64,000 Question"; b) "The $64,000 Challenge"?

* * *

10. Who costarred with Jackie Gleason on the original "Life of Riley" show?

† † †

137.   J'ACCUSE

Who plays:

1.   The accused girl in *Phantom Lady?*

*   *   *

2.   The accused killer in *Cry of the City?*

*   *   *

3.   The accused sailor in *The Lady from Shanghai?*

*   *   *

4.   The accused vet in *The Blue Dahlia?*

*   *   *

5.   The accused prisoner in *Dark Passage?*

*   *   *

6.   The accused housewife in *The Reckless Moment?*

*   *   *

7.   The accused murderer in *Intruder in the Dust?*

*   *   *

8.   The accused murderer in *Face of a Fugitive?*

*   *   *

9.   The accused husband in *Suspicion?*

*   *   *

10.   The accused politician in *The Glass Key?*

138. RADIO KNOW-HOW

1. Who was "loved as much today as ever he was"?

* * *

2. What program presented "facts in the relentless war of the police on the underworld"?

* * *

3. What was the "gigantic stage on which are played a thousand dramas daily"?

* * *

4. Who risked his life "that criminals and racketeers within the law might feel its weight . . ."?

* * *

5. What was "a discussion of books that the world thus far has not been willing or able to let die"?

* * *

6. Whose story reflected the "courage, spirit and integrity of American women everywhere"?

* * *

7. Who was "the most famous Mountie of them all"?

* * *

8. Whose legendary figure galloped "out of the darkness to take up the cause of law and order throughout the West"?

* * *

9. "From the black core of dark Africa" came which colorful figure?

* * *

10. What "tender, human story of young married love was dedicated to everyone who has ever been in love"?

† † †

139.   TOP GUYS

† † † † †

On . . .

1.   January 21, 1924, he died. _____

         *   *   *

2.   November 2, 1930, he became emperor of Ethiopia. _____

         *   *   *

3.   August 14, 1931, he went into exile. _____

         *   *   *

4.   July 5, 1932, he became prime minister of Portugal. _____

         *   *   *

5.   January 30, 1933, he became chancellor of Germany. _____

         *   *   *

6.   September 5, 1933, he became Cuba's ruler. _____

         *   *   *

7.   April 28, 1936, he became king of Egypt. _____

         *   *   *

8.   October 1, 1936, he became chief of the Spanish state. _____

9. December 10, 1936, he abdicated. ———

10. May 10, 1940, he became prime minister of Great Britain. ———

† † †

140. CHANNEL LEADS

✝ ✝ ✝ ✝ ✝

Match the stars with their TV show and role:

1. June Havoc   a) secretary   I. "Doc Corkle"

2. Gale Storm   b) mayor   II. "Honestly Celeste!"

3. Celeste Holm   c) model-agency owner   III. "Meet Millie"

4. Wally Cox   d) editor   IV. "Love That Jill"

5. Robert Sterling   e) dentist   V. "Ichabod and Me"

6. Eddie Mayhoff   f) adventurer   VI. "The Adventure of Hiram Holliday"

7. Jackie Cooper   g) reporter   VII. "Oh! Susanna"

8. Elena Verdugo   h) lawyer   VIII. "Willy"

9. Anne Jeffreys   i) social director   IX. "The People's Choice"

✝ ✝ ✝

141. RADIO ORIGINATORS

Match the radio show and the creator:

1. Frances Crane   a) "The Aldrich Family"
2. Anne Nichols   b) "Mrs. Wiggs of the
                                 Cabbage Patch"
3. Agatha Christie   c) "Betty Boop Fables"
4. Rex Stout   d) "Abbott Mysteries"
5. Raymond Chandler   e) "Abie's Irish Rose
6. Thorne Smith   f) "The Adventures of
                                 Philip Marlow"
7. Clifford Goldsmith   g) "The Adventures of M.
                                 Hercules Poirot"
8. Alice Caldwell Rice   h) "The Adventures of
                                 Nero Wolfe"
9. O. Henry   i) "The Adventures of
                                 Topper"
10. Max Fleischer   j) "Alias Jimmy
                                  Valentine"

142. HEALTHY MEMORIES

Match the medical accomplishment with the discoverer or inventor:

1. Hans Berger, 1929
2. George F. Dick and Gladys H. Dick, 1923
3. Alexander Fleming, 1928
4. George Minot and William Murphy, 1926
5. Manfred J. Sakel, 1929
6. Selman Waksman, 1943
7. Philip Drinker and Louis Shaw, 1928
8. Karl Lansteiner, 1940
9. Joseph Goldberger, 1915

   a) discovered penicillin
   b) invented the iron lung
   c) developed the skin test for scarlet fever
   d) developed insulin-shock treatment for schizophenia
   e) discovered the Rh factor
   f) invented the electroencephalograph
   g) discovered streptomycin
   h) discovered the cure for pellagra
   i) discovered the liver-extract treatment for anemia

143.   THE ONLY BEGETTERS

† † † † †

Match the radio show and the creator of the original work on which it was based:

1. Chic Young
2. George McManus
3. Maxwell Anderson
4. Jan Struther
5. Earl Derr Biggers
6. Alexandre Dumas
7. Chester Gould
8. Burt L. Standish
9. Sax Rohmer
10. Clarence Budington Kelland

a) "Charlie Chan"
b) "Captain Flagg and Sergeant Quirt"
c) "Frank Merriwell"
d) "Blondie"
e) "Hopalong Cassidy"
f) "Dick Tracy"
g) "Fu Manchu"
h) "Bringing Up Father"
i) "The Count of Monte Cristo"
j) "Mrs. Miniver"

† † †

144.   STAMP ACTS

1. A 2¢ red stamp issued at Menlo Park, N.J. on June 5, 1929 commemorated what anniversary?

* * *

2. Three airmail stamps were issued on April 19, 1930 —for 65¢, $1.30, and $2.60. For what purpose were they intended?

* * *

3. Why was a 2¢ red stamp issued at Lake Placid, N.Y. on Jan. 25, 1932?

* * *

4. Why was a 3¢ purple stamp issued on June 15, 1932 at Los Angeles?

* * *

5. On May 25, 1933 a 1¢ green stamp and a 3¢ purple stamp were issued at Chicago, Ill. to commemorate what event?

* * *

6. On August 15, 1933 a purple 3¢ stamp was issued for what "emergency"?

* * *

7. A 3¢ navy-blue stamp was issued on October 9, 1933 for use under very limited conditions. What was its special purpose?

*   *   *

8. The 3¢ purple stamp issued at Boulder City, Nev., on September 30, 1935 commemorated what event?

*   *   *

9. The 3¢ purple stamp issued in San Francisco on February 18, 1939 honored what occasion?

*   *   *

10. The purple 3¢ stamp issued in New York on April 11, 1939 commemorated what event?

*   *   *

11. The three stamps issued on October 16, 1940 in Washington—a 1¢ stamp showing the Statue of Liberty, a 2¢ stamp showing a 90mm AA gun, and a 3¢ stamp showing a torch—were to mark what drive?

145. NETWORK NOSTALGIA

1. Who starred on "Topper"?

* * *

2. Who played Buddy Hackett's girl on "Stanley"?

* * *

3. "Meet Mr. McNutley (later "Meet Mr. McNulty") starred which Oscar-winning actor?

* * *

4. Who played Harrigan on "Harrigan and Son"?

* * *

5. Who played Susie McNamara on "Private Secretary"?

* * *

6. Who played the stage manager in the TV musical version of *Our Town?* Who were the leads?

* * *

7. Who played Duke Mantee in the "Hallmark Hall of Fame" version of *The Petrified Forest?*

* * *

8. What do all these actors have in common: Franchot Tone, Robert Cummings, Edward Arnold, Walter Abel, Norman Fell, Paul Hartman, George Voskovec, Joseph Sweeney, John Beal, Lee Philips, Bart Burns, and Will West?

* * *

9. What Paddy Chayefsky play did Thelma Ritter star in on TV?

* * *

10. Bob Sweeney and Cathy Lewis starred in the TV version of what radio show?

† † †

146.   TV TIME MACHINE

1.   Paul Hartman starred on "Pride of the Family." Who played his wife and his daughter?

* * *

2.   Who starred as Pearson on "Norby"?

* * *

3.   Sherry Alberoni played whose granddaughter?

* * *

4.   Glenn Walker played whose grandson?

* * *

5.   Who played "Young Mr. Bobbin."

* * *

6.   Who played "Jamie"?

* * *

7.   Who played Barry Nelson's wife on "My Favorite Husband"?

* * *

8.   Gertrude Berg was taught by what actor on "Mrs. G. Goes to College"?

* * *

9.   Abby Dalton played whose girl on "Hennessey"?

* * *

10.   Name the cast of "The Phil Silvers Show" and its original name.

† † †

147.   LONG AGO

1.   What do all these people have in common: Richard Gale, Warren Neale, Buck Duane, and Fay Larkin?

*   *   *

2.   Name the famous actor who appeared in all of these "name" movies: *Sadie Thompson, Alias Jimmy Valentine, Arsene Lupin, Rasputin and the Empress, The Late Christopher Bean, The Return of Peter Grimm,* and *The Voice of Bugle Ann.*

*   *   *

3.   What was stolen in *Fast and Loose* . . . in *The Brasher Doubloon?*

*   *   *

4.   Who played both Florence Nightingale and Edith Cavell?

*   *   *

5.   Name the hosts of a) "Hollywood Screen Test"; b) "Star of the Family"; c) "Fashion Magic"; and d) "On Your Way."

*   *   *

6.   "Praise the Lord and Pass the Ammunition" was written by a) Harold Arlen; b) Johnny Mercer; or c) Frank Loesser?

*   *   *

7. General Hugh Johnson directed what government agency?

*   *   *

8. What famous radio series was first broadcast in 1933 over WXYZ?

*   *   *

9. Name the musical comedy that starred Bela Lugosi and Olga Baclanova.

*   *   *

10. Name the boyfriends of these comic-strip characters: a) Tillie the Toiler; b) Betty; c) Sweet Mama; and d) Lil.

†   †   †

148. TV WARM-UP

† † † † †

1. What were the huge prizes on: a) "Grand Slam"; b) "Hollywood Calling"; c) "What's the Name of That Song?"; d) "Take It or Leave It"; e) "Information Please"; f) "Noah Webster Says"; g) "Singo"?

* * *

2. Who hosted: a) "Kitchen Quiz"; b) "Wife Saver"; c) "It Takes a Woman"; d) "Look Your Best"?

* * *

3. "Kookie, Kookie, lend me your comb," was the song identified with what actor on what TV show?

* * *

4. The creator of Joe Palooka was co-host with Johnny Olson on what early TV kid's show?

* * *

5. Who was Tuffy Brasuhn?

* * *

6. Laurie Anders starred on "The Ken Murray Show." Where did Merry Anders work?

* * *

7. Phil Baker hosted "Who's Whose." Art Baker hosted what show?

*   *   *

8.   Edgar Bergen hosted "Do You Trust Your Wife?" On what drama series did Polly Bergen play Helen Morgan?

*   *   *

9.   Mike Connors first starred on "Tightrope!" Chuck Connors starred on what TV show?

*   *   *

10.   Donna Reed had "The Donna Reed Show." What show did Robert Reed appear on?

†   †   †

149. TOTAL RECALL

1. In what 1949 drama was God portrayed as a psychiatrist?

* * *

2. Where did "Young Dr. Malone" live?

* * *

3. What was the name of the famous Cairo hotel burnt down by rioters in 1952?

* * *

4. What was the name of the 1949 treaty that set up NATO?

* * *

5. Shakespeare's *The Tempest* gave a title to a 1932 novel by Aldous Huxley. Name the book.

* * *

6. What was the name of the 1944 economic meeting that set up the International Monetary Fund and the World Bank?

* * *

7. What did Jeanie Macpherson, Frances Marion, June Mathis, and Clara Beranger have in common?

8. Name the Rudolf Besier play about Robert Browning's struggle to rescue his future wife from her father.

*   *   *

9. Name the three leaders who met at the Cairo Conference in 1943.

*   *   *

10. Holden Caulfield was the hero of what 1951 book?

†   †   †

150. TV NAMES

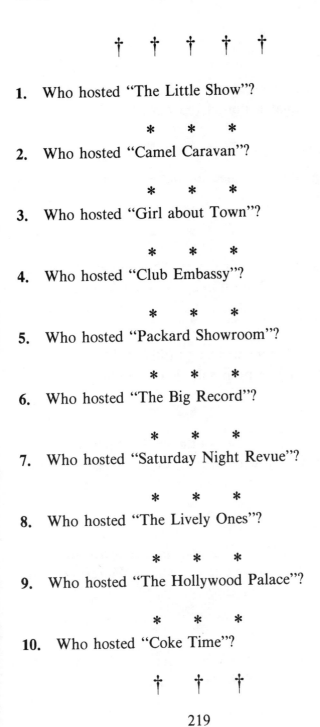

✝ ✝ ✝ ✝ ✝

1. Who hosted "The Little Show"?

* * *

2. Who hosted "Camel Caravan"?

* * *

3. Who hosted "Girl about Town"?

* * *

4. Who hosted "Club Embassy"?

* * *

5. Who hosted "Packard Showroom"?

* * *

6. Who hosted "The Big Record"?

* * *

7. Who hosted "Saturday Night Revue"?

* * *

8. Who hosted "The Lively Ones"?

* * *

9. Who hosted "The Hollywood Palace"?

* * *

10. Who hosted "Coke Time"?

✝ ✝ ✝

151.   WHEN IT ALL HAPPENED

1. What airplane made the first fueled-in-flight non-stop circumnavigation of the world in 1949?

*   *   *

2. What disease killed 20 million people in a 1918 epidemic?

*   *   *

3. What was the name of Sir Thomas Lipton's yacht, in which he tried five times to win the America's Cup?

*   *   *

4. Hawley-Smoot was a) a tariff act, b) a censorship board, c) a peace proposal, or d) a prohibition law?

*   *   *

5. What was the name of the strategic point in Korea that was finally captured by the U.S. in September 1951?

*   *   *

6. Who was the author of *The Franchise Affair:* a) Josephine Tey; b) Agatha Christie; c) Margery Allingham; d) Dorothy Sayers?

*   *   *

7. The 1947 New Look in women's fashions was introduced by a) Chanel, b) Hartnell, c) Dior?

* * *

8. "Newspeak," "unpersons," and "doublethink" are concepts found in what 1949 novel?

* * *

9. Who was the detective in and the author of *The Roman Hat Mystery?*

* * *

10. What is the name of the "accursed" 44-carat blue diamond now in the Smithsonian Institution?

† † †

152. PLEASE STAND BY

1. Name Robert Young's second TV show.

* * *

2. Who played the children on "Father Knows Best"?

* * *

3. What do Jean Hagan and Marjorie Lord have in common?

* * *

4. Who played Leon Ames's wife on "Life with Father"?

* * *

5. Peggy Wood, Dick Van Patten, Rosemary Rici, and Robin Morgan starred on what show?

* * *

6. Who conducted the "Voice of Firestone" orchestra?

* * *

7. Who hosted "Music from Manhattan"?

* * *

8. Who hosted "On the Boardwalk"?

*   *   *

9. Who hosted "The Chevy Showroom"?

*   *   *

10. Who appeared with Betty Ann Grove on "Song Snapshots on a Summer Holiday"?

†   †   †

153. MEMORY IS MADE OF THESE

1. What was the Ch'ing dynasty?

* * *

2. Who was the original bandleader on the "Bob Hope Show"?

* * *

3. What was the name of Arthur Koestler's 1941 novel about the Russian purges of the thirties?

* * *

4. What was the name of the detective in *The House Without a Key* (1925)?

* * *

5. Who were the Chindits?

* * *

6. What was the 1935 Stresa Front?

* * *

7. Name the four novels making up Lawrence Durrell's *Alexandria Quartet*.

* * *

8. Name the writing couple responsible for "Our Gal Sunday," "David Harum," "Lorenzo Jones," "Romance of Helen Trent," and "Stella Dallas."

9. After being "killed" by Moriarity, Sherlock Holmes spent the years before his return in a) New York, b) Tibet, c) Afghanistan, d) Sussex?

10. The *Caine* in *The Caine Mutiny* was a) a battleship, b) a minesweeper, c) a destroyer, d) a submarine, e) an aircraft carrier?

† † †

154. YOU CAN GO BACK AGAIN

1. What is the English title of the German novel, *Im Western nicht Neues?*

* * *

2. The Harry Lime theme was background music in what movie?

* * *

3. What was the code name for the Allied invasion of northwest Africa in 1942?

* * *

4. What is the name of the amateur sleuth who first came on the scene in the book, *The Benson Murder Case?*

* * *

5. What was the Japanese economic program announced by Prime Minister Konoye in 1940?

* * *

6. Name the 1936 novel that took its title from David's lament in 2 Samuel 18:33. Its author?

* * *

7. Name the 1950 novel that took its title from the last words of General Stonewall Jackson. Its author?

* * *

8. Dayton, Tenn. was the scene in 1925 of what event?

* * *

9. Where is Devil's Island?

* * *

10. Name the hill between Naples and Rome, topped by an ancient monastery that was destroyed in World War II.

† † †

155. MEMORIZE THESE

1. What is the English name of Jean-Paul Sartre's 1944 one-act play about a man and two women who have died and are shut up in a room?

* * *

2. What was the name of the German flying manuever developed during World War I that consisted of a half-loop with a half-turn at the top?

* * *

3. What is the name of the German song sung by both sides during World War II?

* * *

4. The Long March was a) The Bonus Army's "invasion" of Washington; b) Huey Long's annual visit to the White House; c) Mao Tse-tung's retreat from Chiang Kai-shek's army; or d) the KKK parade up Pennsylvania Avenue in the twenties?

* * *

5. What was the name of the raft used by Thor Heyerdahl in his voyage from Lima, Peru to the Tuamotu Islands in the Pacific?

* * *

6. MGM film studios was formed by a) Sam Goldwyn; b) Joseph Kennedy; c) Louis B. Mayer; d) Marcus Loew; or e) William Randolph Hearst?

228

*   *   *

7. Where and what is Eniwetok?

*   *   *

8. What was *Freedom 7?*

*   *   *

9. Whose verse was used for the title of James Jones's 1951 Army novel?

*   *   *

10. What was the name of Rommel's army that reinforced the Italians against the British in World War II?

† † †

156. TEAM SPIRIT

† † † † †

Match the ballplayer with his nickname:

1.	John Sigmund Podgajny	a)	Fat Freddie
2.	LeRoy Earl Parmelee	b)	Jockey
3.	Henry Majeski	c)	Specs
4.	Raymond Carl Kolp	d)	Pete
5.	Minter Carney Hayes	e)	Huck
6.	George Aloys Fisher	f)	Sugar
7.	Marrit Patrick Cain	g)	Heeney
8.	Walter Martin Betts	h)	Tarzan
9.	Grover Cleveland Alexander	i)	Showboat
10.	Frederick Landis Fitzsimmons	j)	Jackie

† † †

ANSWERS

✝ ✝ ✝ ✝ ✝

1.

1. *Buck Privates, In the Navy,* and *Abbott and Costello in the Foreign Legion*
2. *In Old Chicago*
3. Veda Ann Borg
4. Ward Bond
5. John Boles
6. Charles Bickford
7. Uncle Matt and Lord Basil Epping
8. Florence Lake
9. b
10. ZaSu Pitts and Patsy Kelly

2.

1-e, 2-a, 3-c, 4-f, 5-h, 6-d, 7-g, 8-i, 9-b

3.

1. *The Crowd Roars*
2. *Bordertown* and *Juarez*
3. *The Road to Singapore*
4. *Love Is on the Air*
5. *Three Men on a Horse*
6. Spike Jones
7. Constantinople
8. Daphne du Maurier
9. Salvador Dali
10. Gregory Peck

4.

1-i, 2-g, 3-h, 4-f, 5-c, 6-e, 7-j, 8-d, 9-a, 10-b

5.

1-e, 2-m, 3-n, 4-f, 5-c, 6-b, 7-l, 8-a, 9-j, 10-g, 11-h, 12-i, 13-d, 14-k

6.

1. A retired Bronx, N.Y. high-school principal who tried to assist in the finding of the Lindbergh baby's kidnapper
2. First president of the Philippine Republic
3. The Antarctic
4. *Four Saints in 3 Acts*
5. Henry Ford
6. c
7. c
8. d
9. Gene Tunney
10. c

7.

1-g, 2-d, 3-m, 4-j, 5-a, 6-c (also Robert Taylor), 7-l, 8-e, 9-i, 10-k, 11-f, 12-h, 13-b

8.

1. "The Plainclothesman"
2. "Doorway to Danger"
3. Lola Albright

4. a) Robert Lansing, b) John Cassavetes, c) Rod Cameron, d) Kent Taylor
5. J. Carrol Naish
6. a) Darren McGavin, b) Ray Milland, c) Ronald Howard, d) David Janssen
7. Harold Humber
8. Raymond Massey
9. Dan Dailey, Vittorio De Sica, Richard Conte, and Jack Hawkins
10. a) Barry Sullivan, b) Barry Nelson, c) Louis Hayward

9.

1-b, 2-d, 3-a, 4-c, 5-c, 6-b, 7-d, 8-b, 9-c, 10-a

10.

1-c-III, IV; 2-e-IV; 3-e-IX, X, V; 4-c-II, I; 5-f-IV; 6-e-VI; 7-b-VII; 8-d-XI; 9-a-XI; 10-c-I; 11-b-I; 12-b-I; 13-a-VIII; 14-g-I

11.

1-c, 2-g, 3-i, 4-e, 5-h, 6-j, 7-a, 8-f, 9-b, 10-d

12.

1-c, 2-j, 3-i, 4-d, 5-f, 6-h, 7-g, 8-a, 9-b, 10-e

13.

1-k, 2-l, 3-f, 4-i, 5-j, 6-h, 7-a, 8-k, 9-k, 10-b, 11-g, 12-m, 13-d, 14-e, 15-c

14.

1-e, 2-c, 3-g, 4-h, 5-f, 6-a, 7-i, 8-d, 9-j, 10-b

15.

1-c, 2-e, 3-g, 4-k, 5-j, 6-m, 7-p, 8-n, 9-i, 10-l, 11-f, 12-h, 13-a, 14-o, 15-d, 16-b

16.

1-e, 2-h, 3-i, 4-b, 5-a, 6-d, 7-c, 8-f, 9-j, 10-g

17.

1. Joseph Cotten
2. Alida Valli
3. Gene Kelly
4. Rita Hayworth
5. Ann Todd
6. Charles Boyer
7. Orson Welles
8. Ida Lupino
9. George Macready
10. Conrad Veidt

18.

1. "America the Beautiful"
2. The Virgin Islands
3. *Of Thee I Sing*
4. b
5. The Carnival of Swing at Randalls' Island, N.Y.
6. d

7. *Panay*
8. They were all record labels.
9. James Cagney

19.

1. Phillips Holmes; Taylor Holmes
2. Jason Robards, Jr.; Jason Robards, Sr.
3. Anthony Perkins; Osgood Perkins
4. John Huston; Walter Huston
5. Peter Fonda; Henry Fonda
6. James Mitchum; Robert Mitchum
7. Leo Gorcey; Bernard Gorcey
8. Tim Holt; Jack Holt
9. Ronald Howard; Leslie Howard
10. Broderick Crawford; Helen Broderick

20.

1. "Omnibus"
2. John Crosby
3. a
4. c
5. Charles Boyer, Dick Powell, Rosalind Russell, and Joel McCrea. Miss Russell and Joel McCrea later departed and David Niven entered.
6. b
7. a) Lyle Bettger, b) Dane Clark, d) Joseph Cotten, d) Jim McKay
8. a) John Howard, b) Warner Anderson, c) Melville Ruick, d) Paul Burke and Vic Rodman (veterinarians)
9. All of them
10. All of them

21.

1. Corey Allen
2. Ed Begley
3. Charles Bickford
4. Richard Boone
5. Ernest Borgnine
6. Raymond Burr
7. Dan Duryea
8. Henry Jones
9. Lee Marvin
10. Walter Slezak

22.

1-d, 2-i, 3-h, 4-b, 5-g, 6-k, 7-j, 8-a, 9-e, 10-c

23.

1-e, 2-f, 3-g, 4-b, 5-d, 6-h, 7-a, 8-c

24.

1. Lou Boudreau
2. The next day, May 31, 1927, Johnny Neun, Detroit first baseman, made it against the Cleveland Indians. It hasn't happened since.
3. Martin, Dean, Collins, and Durocher
4. They went south, to play in the Mexican League.
5. President of the National League for 18 years
6. Dick Sisler; George Sisler
7. Ralph Branca
8. Tommy Henrich
9. The Browns
10. Cleveland Indians in 1954

25.

1. a
2. b
3. a
4. Lon Chaney, Sr.
5. Henry Hull
6. J. Carrol Naish
7. b
8. c
9. d
10. b

26.

1-h, 2-g, 3-b, 4-f, 5-a, 6-c, 7-e, 8-i, 9-d

27.

1-c, 2-j, 3-f, 4-i, 5-h, 6-d, 7-e, 8-a, 9-g, 10-b

28.

1-j, 2-a, 3-c, 4-i, 5-e, 6-d, 7-f, 8-g, 9-h, 10-b

29.

1-e, 2-b, 3-f, 4-g, 5-h, 6-a, 7-i, 8-c, 9-j, 10-d

30.

1. Gen. Smedley Butler, Benito Mussolini
2. Nicholas Murray Butler and Jane Addams
3. Rev. Harry Emerson Fosdick
4. Theodore Dreiser and Sinclair Lewis

5. Alfred E. Smith
6. Nine Alabama blacks accused of rape; eight were sentenced to death.
7. Knute Rockne
8. Lily Pons
9. The Vatican; Pope Pius XI
10. Rogers Hornsby

31.

1-b, 2-c, 3-b, 4-c, 5-b, 6-c, 7-c, 8-a, 9-b, 10-a

32.

1. They were all hosts, with the exception of Ralph Edwards.
2. a) opera, b) baseball, c) art, d) Shakespeare
3. "Jukebox Jury"
4. "Answer Yes or No"
5. "Who Said That?"
6. d
7. "Judge for Yourself"
8. a) "Search for Tomorrow," b) "Hawkins Falls," c) "Valiant Lady"
9. They were all, at one time or the other, part of Lassie's family
10. "Fury"

33.

1-j, 2-l, 3-d, 4-h, 5-i, 6-k, 7-b, 8-c, 9-m, 10-a, 11-g, 12-f, 13-e

34.

1-b, 2-i, 3-d, 4-c, 5-j, 6-a, 7-f, 8-e, 9-h, 10-g

35.

1-g, 2-c, 3-k, 4-b, 5-f, 6-d, 7-e, 8-a, 9-i, 10-h, 11-j

36.

1. Trombone
2. Alto sax
3. Tenor sax
4. Clarinet
5. Piano
6. Guitar
7. Drums
8. Bass
9. Violin
10. Soprano sax, baritone sax, bass sax

37.

1. Hattie Wyett Caraway (Dem., Ark.)
2. Jim Londos
3. The protagonists of *The Good Earth*
4. Crack tennis player
5. Sigmund Spaeth
6. Balloonist who went into the stratosphere
7. Submariner who explored the bottom of the sea
8. Amelia Earhart, first woman to solo the Atlantic
9. Painter of *American Gothic*
10. Characters played by Clark Gable and Norma Shearer in *Strange Interlude*

38.

1-a-VII, 2-d-II, 3-e-VIII, 4-d-I, 5-d-III, 6-a-VII, 7-d-IV, 8-c-IX, 9-c-V, 10-f-II, 11-b-VI

39.

1-c, 2-g, 3-a, 4-e, 5-f, 6-j, 7-b, 8-d, 9-h, 10-i

40.

1. *Escape,* Ethel Vance
2. Sholem Asch, *The Nazarene*
3. Jan Struther, *Mrs. Miniver*
4. Osa Johnson, *I Married Adventure*
5. *The White Cliffs*
6. Marcia Davenport, *The Valley of Decision*
7. Elizabeth Goudge, *Green Dolphin Street*
8. Lillian Smith's *Strange Fruit*
9. Quentin Reynolds
10. John Roy Carlson

41.

1-j, 2-d, 3-f, 4-g, 5-h, 6-c, 7-a, 8-e, 9-b, 10-i

42.

1. Assassin of Chicago Mayor Anton Cermak
2. FDR's 45-foot sailboat
3. First woman governor (Wyoming) and the first woman director of the Mint
4. Wendell L. Willkie
5. They were all kidnapped in 1933.

6. They were all attractions at Chicago's World's Fair.
7. The destruction of the *Akron,* the Navy dirigible; in all, 73 people lost their lives.
8. Mr. and Mrs. Charles Lindbergh
9. 1933
10. John Farrow

43.

1-c, 2-f, 3-g, 4-j, 5-b, 6-a, 7-h, 8-e, 9-d, 10-i

44.

1. Ray Anthony
2. Mildred Bailey
3. Pearl Bailey
4. La Vern Baker
5. Dave Barbour
6. Charlie Barnet
7. Count Basie
8. Bix Beiderbecke
9. Eubie Blake
10. Joe Bushkin

45.

1-c, 2-d, 3-a, 4-h, 5-g, 6-f, 7-b, 8-e, 9-i

46.

1. Viña Delmar
2. "The Motor Boys"
3. "The Moving Picture Girls"

4. "The Bobbsey Twins"
5. "The Boy Scouts"
6. "Tom Swift"
7. "The Hardy Boys"
8. Robert W. Service
9. c
10. a

47.

1-g, 2-e, 3-f, 4-a, 5-h, 6-j, 7-i, 8-c, 9-d, 10-b

48.

1-e, 2-c, 3-j, 4-k, 5-a, 6-d, 7-b, 8-f, 9-g, 10-h, 11-i

49.

1. *Desert Desperadoes*
2. *The Desert Fox* and *The Desert Rats*
3. *Desert Fury*
4. *The Desert Hawk*
5. *Desert Hell*
6. *Desert Legion*
7. *Desert Patrol*
8. "The Riff Song" and "One Alone"
9. *Sons of the Desert*
10. *Desert Sands*

50.

1. "Air Adventures of Jimmy Allen"
2. Fury
3. "Flying Patrol"

    4. Hop Harrigan
    5. "Howie Wing"
    6. Roosty
    7. "Sky King"
    8. "Smilin' Jack"
    9. Mallory
    10. Wings Cigarettes

51.

1-d, 2-f, 3-j, 4-g, 5-i, 6-h, 7-a, 8-b, 9-e, 10-c

52.

1-d, 2-e, 3-i, 4-b, 5-j, 6-g, 7-h, 8-a, 9-c, 10-f

53.

Kay Francis

54.

1-g-II, 2-a-V, 3-f-IV, 4-d-VII, 5-e-I, 6-c-VIII, 7-h-VI, 8-b-III

55.

1-d, 2-f, 3-b, 4-h, 5-j, 6-i, 7-g, 8-c, 9-a, 10-e

56.

1-j, 2-d, 3-i, 4-e, 5-k, 6-b, 7-c, 8-g, 9-a, 10-h

57.

1-g, 2-h, 3-f, 4-e, 5-d, 6-c, 7-b, 8-k, 9-a, 10-i, 11-j

58.

1-h-III, 2-e-VIII, 3-b-IV, 4-d-V, 5-g-VI, 6-f-I, 7-c-VII, 8-a-II

59.

1-h, 2-b, 3-e, 4-i, 5-d, 6-c, 7-g, 8-j, 9-a, 10-f

60.

1-e, 2-f, 3-a, 4-c, 5-i, 6-j, 7-k, 8-l, 9-b, 10-g, 11-h, 12-d

61.

1-f, 2-h, 3-a, 4-c, 5-e, 6-j, 7-g, 8-d, 9-b, 10-i

62.

1-e, 2-a, 3-o, 4-g, 5-k, 6-i, 7-b, 8-j, 9-c, 10-f, 11-n, 12-h, 13-l, 14-d, 15-m

63.

1-b, 2-f, 3-k, 4-g, 5-h, 6-i, 7-e, 8-c, 9-d, 10-a, 11-j

64.

1. *100,000,000 Guinea Pigs*
2. James Hilton's *Goodbye, Mr. Chips*

3. Mary Ellen Chase
4. *Brazilian Adventure*
5. *The Life of Our Lord*
6. Rachel Field
7. *Around the World in Eleven Years*
8. *Live Alone and Like It; Orchids on Your Budget*
9. *And Tell of Time*
10. *The Importance of Living*

65.

1-a, 2-a, 3-a, 4-b, 5-b, 6-c, 7-a, 8-a, 9-b, 10-c, 11-c

66.

1-e, 2-g, 3-j, 4-c, 5-h, 6-i, 7-k, 8-b, 9-d, 10-a, 11-f

67.

Ann Harding

68.

1-d, 2-e, 3-b, 4-f, 5-a, 6-g, 7-h, 8-c, 9-i

69.

1. Edna Ferber; *So Big* (1924) and *Cimarron* (1930)
2. *The Woman of Andros*
3. *Years of Grace* by Margaret Ayer Barnes
4. Mary Roberts Rinehart wrote *The Door.*
5. Hugh Walpole. His first book in the series was *Rogue Herries*

245

6. *Story of San Michele*
7. *Education of a Princess* by Grand Duchess Marie
8. *Washington Merry-Go-Round* by Drew Pearson and Robert Allen
9. Ely Culbertson wrote *Culbertson's Summary* and *Contract Bridge Blue Book.*
10. *A Fortune to Share*

70.

Marie Dressler

71.

1. Barbour
2. San Francisco
3. Fanny
4. Paul
5. Aviator
6. In an attic
7. His adopted daughter
8. Bill Herbert and Dan Murray
9. Hank and Pinky
10. Capt. Nicholas (Nicky) Lacy
11. Cliff
12. Irene Franklin
13. Betty
14. Six daughters

72.

1-d, 2-j, 3-e, 4-f, 6-a, 7-c, 8-g, 9-b, 10-h, 11-i

73.

   1932 Klein, Philadelphia
   1933 Hubbell, New York
   1934 Dean, St. Louis
   1935 Hartnett, Chicago
   1936 Hubbell, New York
   1937 Medwick, St. Louis
   1938 Lombardi, Cincinnati
   1939 Walters, Cincinnati
   1940 McCormick, Cincinnati
   1941 Camilli, Brooklyn

74.

   1-e, 2-f, 3-b, 4-j, 5-i, 6-d, 7-a, 8-h, 9-g, 10-c

75.

   1-d, 2-a, 3-b, 4-c, 5-e, 6-j, 7-i, 8-h, 9-g, 10-f

76.

   1-e, 2-g, 3-f, 4-h, 5-b, 6-a, 7-i, 8-j, 9-d, 10-c

77.

   1. Stephen Foster and P. T. Barnum
   2. Howard Hughes
   3. A radio program, also known as "The Carborundum Hour"
   4. John D. Rockefeller, Sr.
   5. Joe Louis
   6. a

7. b
8. b
9. d
10. d

78.

1-h, 2-e, 3-d, 4-b, 5-j, 6-i, 7-f, 8-a, 9-g, 10-c

79.

1932 Foxx, Philadelphia
1933 Foxx, Philadelphia
1934 Cochrane, Detroit
1935 Greenberg, Detroit
1936 Gehrig, New York
1937 Gehringer, Detroit
1938 Foxx, Boston
1939 DiMaggio, New York
1940 Greenberg, Detroit
1941 DiMaggio, New York

80.

1-e, 2-i, 3-d, 4-g, 5-h, 6-f, 7-c, 8-g, 9-j, 10-b

81.

1-i, 2-g, 3-a, 4-f, 5-h, 6-b, 7-d, 8-e, 9-c, 10-j

82.

1-d, 2-d, 3-a, 4-c, 5-a, 6-c, 7-c, 8-c, 9-a, 10-d, 11-d

83.

1. Mickey Spillane
2. A. C. Spectorsky
3. Herbert A. Philbrick
4. Vance Packard
5. Pat Boone
6. Morton Thompson
7. William L. Shirer
8. Richard Wright
9. Lloyd C. Douglas
10. Marjorie Kinnan Rawlings
11. Kenneth Roberts
12. Louis Bromfield
13. Walter D. Edmonds
14. Carl Sandburg
15. John Gunther
16. William Saroyan

84.

1. Jim Corrigan
2. Kent Nelson
3. The Blackhawks
4. Dave Nelson
5. Sky Wolf
6. Von Emmelman
7. Diana Prince

85.

1-b, 2-d, 3-g, 4-i, 5-j, 6-f, 7-c, 8-h, 9-a, 10-e

86.

1. 1946
2. 1944
3. 1945
4. 1943

87.

1. Peter Lawford
2. Janet Leigh
3. Mario Lanza
4. Deborah Kerr
5. Van Johnson
6. Leon Ames
7. Mary Astor
8. Jeanette MacDonald
9. Barry Fitzgerald
10. Ava Gardner

88.

1. "America's Town Meeting"
2. Vincent Lopez
3. "Bob Elson Aboard the Century"
4. "Chicago Theatre of the Air"
5. Father Charles E. Coughlin
6. "Fun in Swing Time"
7. "Grand Old Opry" (also Dixie Tabernacle, War Memorial Auditorium)
8. "The Musical Steelmakers"

89.

1. *Raffles, the Amateur Cracksman*
2. *Sherlock Holmes*

3. *Beau Brummel*
4. *Tempest*
5. *The Beloved Rogue*
6. *The Man from Blankley's*
7. *Svengali*
8. *The Mad Genius* .
9. *Arsene Lupin*
10. *Dinner at Eight*

90.

1-d, 2-g, 3-h, 4-i, 5-a, 6-e, 7-j, 8-f, 9-b, 10-c

91.

1-c, 2-d, 3-g, 4-f, 5-j, 6-h, 7-b, 8-i, 9-a, 10-e

92.

1. *Arrowsmith*
2. *The Man Who Broke the Bank at Monte Carlo*
3. *A Tale of Two Cities*
4. *Lost Horizon*
5. *The Prisoner of Zenda*
6. *If I Were King*
7. *The Light That Failed*
8. *The Talk of the Town*
9. *Random Harvest*
10. *The Late George Apley*

93.

1. H. B. Wright
2. Kathleen Norris

251

3. Gene Stratton Porter
4. J. C. Ferris
5. Victor Appleton

94.

1. They were all Brain Trusters.
2. $25 a week
3. Haakon VII
4. Tempos
5. L Orders cut production of nonessential items; M Orders allocated raw materials.
6. A stickers received the lowest gas allotment, three gallons a week; B stickers were for cars used for essential driving; C stickers were for cars used in essential activities.
7. Ground Observer Corps—civilian aircraft spotters
8. Twin-engined B-25's
9. Major General Alexander A. Vandegrift
10. 8th Army

95.

1. a
2. Lucille Ball
3. Edward Arnold
4. Dana Andrews
5. Philip Ahn
6. Stephen Foster
7. a
8. c
9. Buffalo Bill
10. Winston Churchill

96.

1-c, 2-d, 3-j(!), 4-e, 5-a, 6-b, 7-h, 8-g, 9-i, 10-f

97.

1-b, 2-i, 3-f, 4-g, 5-e, 6-h, 7-c, 8-j, 9-a, 10-d

98.

1. Office of Price Administration-d
2. War Production Board-e
3. War Labor Board-c
4. War Manpower Commission-i
5. War Relocation Authority-f
6. Office of War Information-g
7. War Shipping Administration-h
8. Office of War Mobilization-a
9. Office of Scientific Research and Development-b
10. Office of Defense Transportation-j

99.

1-d-I, 2-h-IV, 3-b-X, 4-c-IX, 5-g-VIII, 6-j-VII, 7-f-VI, 8-i-III, 9-a-II, 10-e-V

100.

1-k, 2-f, 3-i, 4-l, 5-j, 6-e, 7-a, 8-c, 9-d, 10-h, 11-g, 12-b

101.

1-j, 2-h, 3-g, 4-i, 5-d, 6-c, 7-b, 8-f, 9-a, 10-e

102.

1. Larry Funk
2. Richard Himber
3. Yes. Richard Kollmar came later.
4. Characters from Ed McConnell's stories on "The Buster Brown Gang" show
5. Mel Blanc
6. "Chandu the Magician"
7. Walter Connolly, Santos Ortega, and Ed Begley
8. a) Pedro, b) Frankie Remley, c) Beetle and Bottle, d) The Mad Russian
9. a) Rev. Charles E. Fuller, b) Rev. Ralph Sockman, c) Rev. Harry Emerson Fosdick, d) Rev. Walter A. Maier
10. Sondra Deel

103.

1. *The Dark Mirror*
2. *The Dark Past*
3. *Dark Hazard*
4. *The Dark Horse*
5. *Dark Command*
6. *The Dark Corner*
7. *The Dark Angel*
8. *Dark City*
9. *Dark Passage*
10. *Dark Victory*

104.

1-g, 2-i, 3-h, 4-b, 5-c, 6-d, 7-e, 8-j, 9-a, 10-f

105.

1. The moon
2. The League of Nations
3. Frank Yerby, Russell Janney, Mary Jane Ward
4. Bikini Atoll
5. The Philippines
6. President Franklin D. Roosevelt
7. Commerce Secretary Henry Wallace
8. John D. Rockefeller, Jr.
9. Frances Xavier Cabrini
10. Cincinnati and Brooklyn

106.

1. *Come and Get it.*
2. *Come Fill the Cup*
3. *Come Back, Little Sheba*
4. *Go Into Your Dance*
5. *Go for Broke!*
6. *Go West*
7. *Going My Way*
8. *Go West, Young Man*
9. *Come to the Stable*
10. *Come Live with Me*

107.

1. Charles Van Doren
2. Fess Parker
3. She claimed she was Bridey Murphy.
4. Haircuts

5. Teresa Brewer
6. The Ames Brothers
7. Jonie James
8. Kitty Kallen
9. Al Martino
10. Georgia Gibbs

108.

1-k, 2-b, 3-j, 4-d, 5-c, 6-i, 7-g, 8-f, 9-h, 10-d (ah, there, #4!), 11-a, 12-e

109.

1-c, 2-l, 3-k, 4-j, 5-i, 6-h, 7-g, 8-f, 9-e, 10-d, 11-a, 12-b

110.

1. a) Luckies, b) Camels, c) Chesterfields, d) Old Golds
2. Benny Goodman, b) Fred Waring, Glenn Miller; c) Tommy Dorsey; d) Artie Shaw
3. a) Tex Williams, b) Cab Calloway, c) Ben Pollack, d) Fred Waring, Benny Goodman; e) Red Ingle; f) Glen Gray; g) Vincent Lopez
4. Picayune
5. Menthorets
6. They cost 10¢ a pack.
7. Old Gold

111.

1-e, 2-i, 3-a, 4-k, 5-j, 6-g, 7-d, 8-b, 9-c, 10-f, 11-h

112.

1. None of these. It was won twice by Rogers Hornsby and Ted Williams, though.
2. Tony Lazzeri, N.Y. Yankees, May 24, 1936
3. They stopped Joe DiMaggio's 56-game hitting spree, July 17, 1941. Smith was the starting pitcher, Bagby was relief, and third baseman Keltner caught two DiMaggio hits.
4. He struck out the side in both the first and second innings.
5. Bob Feller, April 16, 1960, Chicago White Sox vs. Cleveland Indians
6. Johnny Vander Meer (Cincinnati Reds) in 1938, against the Boston Braves and the Brooklyn Dodgers
7. In the third game of the 1932 Yankee-Cub Series

8 and 9. Bill McKechnie

10. Joe Nuxhall, Cincinnati Reds, 15

113.

1-c, 2-d, 3-g, 4-h, 5-i, 6-b, 7-f, 8-a, 9-e, 10-j

114.

1. Henry Ford
2. c
3. a
4. Generals Arnold, Eisenhower, MacArthur, and Marshall; Admirals King, Leahy, and Nimitz
5. Carlo Tresca
6. Ignace Jan Paderewski of Poland
7. France

8. c
9. a
10. Bobby Feller

115.

1-d, 2-h, 3-j, 4-c, 5-i, 6-f, 7-g, 8-e, 9-a, 10-b

116.

1. Neil Hamilton
2. Morton Downey
3. Ilka Chase
4. Kathy Godfrey
5. Eddie Condon

117.

1. *The Country Doctor*
2. Both played by Ray Collins
3. "Dr. Christian"
4. Selena Royle
5. "Joyce Jordan, M.D."
6. "The Life and Love of Dr. Susan"
7. Clubfoot
8. "The Road to Life"
9. They were both "strange."
10. They were all characters appearing one time or another on "Valiant Lady."

118.

1. Eddie Albert
2. Calamity Jane

3. Bulldog Drummond
4. a) Peter Lawford, b) Jack Lemmon, c) Howard Duff, d) Wendell Corey, e) Eddie Albert
5. Pat O'Brien
6. Rin Tin Tin
7. Loretta Young
8. Mary Astor
9. Barbara Stanwyck
10. Ann Sheridan

119.

1. Theodore Bilbo
2. It was the Freedom Train, bearing a collection of treasured historical documents, and making stops across the country.
3. The UN flag
4. The streetcars stopped running.
5. Flying saucers
6. Grace Moore and Prince Gustaf Adolf of Sweden
7. They were sites of disasters.
8. a) Bernard De Voto, b) Laura Z. Hobson, c) Sinclair Lewis, d) Kenneth Roberts, e) Faith Baldwin, f) James A. Michener, g) Edison Marshall
9. Charlie Chaplin
10. Margaret Truman

120.

1-g, 2-c, 3-h, 4-b, 5-d, 6-i, 7-f, 8-e, 9-a, 10-j

121.

1. Vincent Price hosted "ESP."
2. Norman Brokenshire
3. They all appeared on the "Today" show.
4. Connie Russell, Jack Haskell, and Cliff Norton
5. Walter Cronkite
6. Andy Williams, Steve Lawrence, and Eydie Gorme
7. "Bank on the Stars"
8. "Johnny Carson Show," "Earn Your Vacation," and "Who Do You Trust"?
9. "The Chesterfield Supper Club"
10. Bob Howard

122.

1-i, 2-h, 3-g, 4-c, 5-f, 6-b, 7-e, 8-a, 9-d, 10-j

123.

1-e, 2-b, 3-i, 4-j, 5-d, 6-h, 7-g, 8-f, 9-c, 10-a

124.

1. a) "Adorable"; b) "Bows"; c) "Gusta"; d) "Magic"
2. Westminster
3. Mt. Palomar, Calif.
4. Idlewild Airport, N.Y.
5. American Federation of Musicians
6. a) Dwight D. Eisenhower, b) Dale Carnegie, c) Thomas Merton, d) Lloyd Douglas, e) Norman Mailer, f) Ross Lockridge, g) A. J. Cronin, h) Irwin Shaw

7. a) *Johnny Belinda,* b) *The Red Shoes,* c) *Red River*
8. Judge Harold R. Medina
9. The Displaced Persons Act
10. "Judy Splinters" was a puppet; "The Masked Spooner" was a West Coast mystery singer.

125.

1-c, 2-g, 3-l, 4-d, 5-b, 6-k, 7-e, 8-j, 9-a, 10-i, 11-f, 12-h

126.

1-b, 2-c, 3-d, 4-c, 5-c, 6-d, 7-b, 8-c, 9-c, 10-d

127.

1. Robin Chandler
2. Rod Steiger and Nancy Marchand
3. Bud Collyer
4. Clifton Fadiman
5. Herb Shriner
6. Joan Davis
7. Gale Storm
8. Marie Wilson; Cathy Lewis was the girlfriend.
9. "Mr. and Mrs. North"
10. Red Buttons

128.

1. a
2. Lawson Little

3. The Original Celtics
4. He is the only man to have won the Wimbledon singles championship three times (1934, 1935, 1936).
5. For his wrong-way run in the 1929 Rose Bowl game (University of California vs. Georgia Tech); he was center for the Golden Bears.
6. The highest score ever in the NFL championship game (Chicago Bears beat the Washington Redskins 73–0).
7. The same 1924 team: Charlie Collins and Ed Huntsinger, ends; Rip Miller and Joe Bach, tackles; Noble Kizer and John Weibel, guards; Adam Walsh, center
8. Jersey City
9. Jack Sharkey

129.

1-b, 2-c, 3-k, 4-l, 5-a, 6-j, 7-i, 8-h, 9-g, 10-d, 11-e, 12-f

130.

1. Jack Benny's show
2. "All Star Revue"
3. "The Saturday Night Revue"
4. First Martha Stewart, then Vivian Blaine
5. "Fireball Fun for All"
6. Henny Youngman and Rocky Graziano appeared, along with singer Marion Colby.
7. Edgar Bergen
8. First Jeff Donnell, later Phyllis Avery

9. Nancy Ames
10. Arlene Francis

131.
1. The psychopath in *M*
2. Eugene O'Neill's *The Long Voyage Home,* directed by John Ford
3. Don Ameche
4. Eric Ambler
5. June Allyson
6. John Agar
7. They were all film directors.
8. Deafness
9. Split personality
10. They both had amnesia.

132.
1. Ozzie Nelson and Harriet Hilliard
2. "Amanda of Honeymoon Hill"
3. "The American Album of Familiar Music"
4. "Armstrong of the SBI"
5. Tallulah Bankhead
6. "Big Sister"
7. "Brighter Day"
8. "The Colgate Sports Newsreel starring Bill Stern"
9. "Dr. I.Q."
10. "Favorite Story"

133.

1-d, 2-g, 3-a, 4-j, 5-i, 6-h, 7-k, 8-l, 9-c, 10-f, 11-e, 12-b

134.

1-e, 2-i, 3-c, 4-g, 5-b, 6-j, 7-h, 8-d, 9-f, 10-a

135.

1. They all played governesses: Deborah Kerr in *The Chalk Garden,* Bette Davis in *All This and Heaven, Too,* and Joan Fontaine in *Jane Eyre.*
2. They all played Doc Holliday: Cesar Romero in *Frontier Marshal,* Walter Huston in *The Outlaw,* Victor Mature in *My Darling Clementine,* and Kirk Douglas in *Gunfight at the OK Corral.*
3. They both played hypnotists: Orson Welles in *Black Magic,* Jose Ferrer in *Whirlpool.*
4. They all played Jesse James: Tyrone Power in *Jesse James,* Lawrence Tierney in *Badman's Territory,* Macdonald Carey in *The Great Missouri Raid,* and Audie Murphy in *Kansas Raiders.*
5. They all played Jane Eyre, who was a governess.
6. They all played Mr. Rochester.
7. They were all Joan of Arc at one time or another.
8. They all played Julius Caesar.
9. They're all the same person!

136.

1. a) Jack Barry, b) Paul Trippe, c) Peter Donald
2. Bergen Evans
3. Bud Collyer
4. Ray Heatherton
5. Jimmie Dodd
6. "Wagon Train"
7. Clint Walker
8. Hugh O'Brian
9. a) Hal March, b) Ralph Story
10. Rosemary DeCamp

137.

1. Ella Raines
2. Richard Conte
3. Orson Welles
4. Alan Ladd
5. Humphrey Bogart
6. Joan Bennett
7. Juano Hernandez
8. Fred MacMurray
9. Cary Grant
10. Brian Donlevy

138.

1. Frank Merriwell
2. "Gangbusters"
3. "Grand Central Station"
4. "The Green Hornet"
5. "Invitation to Learning"
6. "Portia Faces Life"
7. "Silver Eagle"
8. "Straight Arrow"

9. Tarzan
10. "When a Girl Marries"

139.
1. Lenin
2. Haile Selassie
3. King Alfonso XIII of Spain
4. Antonio de Salazar
5. Adolf Hitler
6. Fulgencio Batista
7. Farouk
8. Francisco Franco
9. Edward VIII
10. Winston Churchill

140.
1-h-IX, 2-i-VII, 3-g-II, 4-f-VI, 5-d-V, 6-e-I, 7-b-IX, 8-a-III, 9-c-IV

141.
1-d, 2-e, 3-g, 4-h, 5-f, 6-i, 7-a, 8-b, 9-j, 10-c

142.
1-f, 2-c, 3-a, 4-i, 5-d, 6-g, 7-b, 8-e, 9-h

143.
1-d, 2-h, 3-b, 4-j, 5-a, 6-i, 7-f, 8-c, 9-g, 10-e

144.

1. Fiftieth anniversary of Edison's electric lamp
2. For use on mail carried on the first Europe–American round-trip flight of the Graf Zeppelin
3. To honor the International Olympic Winter Games
4. In honor of the Los Angeles Olympics
5. The Century of Progress International Exposition
6. To drum up support for the NRA
7. It was limited to use on letters mailed through the post office of the Little America base in Antarctica.
8. The completion of Boulder Dam
9. The opening of the Golden Gate International Exposition
10. The opening of the New York's World's Fair
11. National Defense

145.

1. Leo G. Carrol, Anne Jeffreys, and Robert Sterling
2. Carol Burnett
3. Ray Milland
4. Pat O'Brien
5. Ann Sothern
6. Frank Sinatra; Eva Marie Saint and Paul Newman
7. Humphrey Bogart
8. They were the jury in the TV production of *Twelve Angry Men.*
9. *The Catered Affair*
10. "Fibber McGee and Molly"

146.

1. Fay Wray, Natalie Wood
2. David Wayne
3. Ed Wynn's
4. Charlie Ruggles's ("The World of Mr. Sweeney")
5. Jackie Kelk
6. Brandon de Wilde
7. Joan Caulfield, later Vanessa Brown
8. Sir Cedric Hardwicke
9. Jackie Cooper's
10. Harvey Lembeck, Maurice Gosfield, Paul Ford, Herbie Faye, Elizabeth Fraser, and Billy Sands; "You'll Never Get Rich"

147.

1. They are all characters in Zane Grey novels.
2. Lionel Barrymore
3. a Shakespearean manuscript, a coin
4. Anna Neagle
5. a) Neil Hamilton, b) Morton Downey, c) Ilka Chase, d) Kathy Godfrey
6. c
7. NRA
8. "The Lone Ranger"
9. *Murder at the Vanities*
10. a) Mac, b) Lester De Pester, c) Barney Google, d) Jungle Jim

148.

1. a) $100 Savings Bond, b) $30,000 in prizes, c) $5 and up, d) $64, e) a set of the *Encyclopaedia*

Britannica, f) $2 for a list of five difficult words and for each correct answer, g) $4
2. a) Ed and Polly East, b) Allen Prescott, c) Frances Scott, d) Richard Willis
3. Ed "Kookie" Byrnes on "77 Sunset Strip"
4. "Kids and Company"
5. A Roller Derby star
6. "How to Marry a Millionaire"
7. "You Asked for It"
8. "Playhouse 90"
9. "The Rifleman"
10. "The Defenders"

149.

1. *The Cocktail Party*
2. Three Oaks
3. Shepheard's
4. The Atlantic Pact
5. *Brave New World* ("O brave new world, that has such people in't.")
6. Bretton Woods Conference
7. They all wrote for the silent screen.
8. *The Barretts of Wimpole Street*
9. Franklin Delano Roosevelt, Winston Churchill, and Chiang Kai-shek
10. *The Catcher in the Rye*

150.

1. John Conte
2. Vaughn Monroe
3. Kyle MacDonnell
4. Mindy Carson

5. Martha Wright
6. Patti Page
7. Hoagy Carmichael
8. Vic Damone
9. Bing Crosby
10. Eddie Fisher

151.
1. The B-29 Superfortress
2. The Spanish flu
3. *The Shamrock*
4. a
5. Heartbreak Ridge
6. a
7. c
8. *1984*
9. Ellery Queen
10. The Hope Diamond

152.
1. "Window on Main Street"
2. Elinor Donahue (Betty), Lauren Chapin (Kathy), Billy Gray (Bud)
3. They've both played Danny Thomas's wife.
4. Lurene Tuttle
5. "Mama"
6. Howard Barlow
7. Sammy Kaye
8. Paul Whiteman
9. Pat Boone and Andy Williams
10. Merv Griffin

153.

1. The last imperial dynasty to rule in China (1644–1912)
2. Skinnay Ennis
3. *Darkness at Noon*
4. Charlie Chan
5. A British unit that fought behind the Japanese lines in Burma during World War II
6. A short-lived pact formed against Germany by France, Britain—and Italy
7. *Justine, Mountolive, Balthazar,* and *Clea*
8. Ann and Frank Hummert
9. b
10. b

154.

1. *All Quiet on the Western Front*
2. *The Third Man*
3. Torch
4. Philo Vance
5. The Greater East Asia Co-Prosperity Sphere
6. *Absalom, Absalom!,* William Faulkner
7. *Across the River and into the Trees,* Ernest Hemingway
8. The Scopes trial; J. T. Scopes was found guilty of teaching Darwinism and fined $100.
9. Off French Guiana; the French government closed the island in 1953.
10. Monte Cassino

155.

1. *No Exit*
2. Immelmann Turn

3. "Lili Marlene"
4. c
5. *Kontiki*
6. d
7. An atoll in the Marshall Islands, the scene of the first H-bomb blast, November 1, 1952
8. Alan Shepard's spacecraft, which made one orbit of the Earth in 1961
9. Kipling: "Gentlemen-rankers out on the spree,/ Damned from here to eternity."
10. Afrika Korps

156.

1-c, 2-h, 3-g, 4-b, 5-j, 6-i, 7-f, 8-e, 9-d, 10-a